/VVVVVVVVVVVV\

MARCHBANKS'
ALMANACK

/VVVVVVVVVVVV\

an Astrological and Inspirational

Conta ...

Secret ...

How ...

*Fortune-Telling by the Disposition
of Moles on the Body
and divers other arcane knowledge
here revealed for the First Time;*

*

AS WELL AS

*

Generous Extracts from the Correspondence,
Pensées, Musings, *Obiter Dicta*
and Ruminations of Wizard Marchbanks.

❖✦❖✦❖✦❖✦❖✦❖✦❖

*The star-led Wizard
hastes with odours sweet!*

MILTON

*

Marchbanks' Almanack

Robertson Davies

INTRODUCTION: *Gordon Roper*
GENERAL EDITOR: *Malcolm Ross*

New Canadian Library No. 61

The Canadian Publishers

*

McClelland and Stewart Limited
25 Hollinger Road, Toronto

*

Printed and bound in Canada

CONTENTS

CONTENTS

CONTENTS

CONTENTS

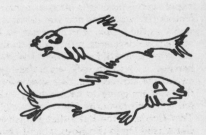

INTRODUCTION

EARLY ONE JUNE EVENING, now twenty-two years ago, after a dinner spiced with Marchbanks tabletalk, my hosts and I talked for awhile on the verandah of Marchbanks Towers before I went on my way to see my wife and new son in the Peterborough Civic Hospital. The following Saturday evening I did what many Peterborough people did in those days—opened the *Peterborough Examiner* at the editorial page to read "The Diary of Samuel Marchbanks." The Tuesday entry ran:

> Was chatting today with a man who had just had a baby; that is to say, his wife actually had the baby, but as anyone knows who has experienced it, the work of the superintending of such a process is often as exhausting as that of the mother. He was weak and run down, and subject to dizzy spells, as the people who have just had babies always are in the advertisements, so I urged him to get himself a good nerve tonic, and did what I could to revive him with strawberries. . . . As men will, when they get together, we discussed the curious fact, that whenever it becomes known that you are going to have a baby, everybody hastens to tell you their favourite Horrible Tale about the Baby with Two Heads, or the Baby that Vanished, or the Baby that Got Mixed Up in the Hospital and never knew whether it was a boy or a girl. Everybody likes to scare the wits out of an expectant father. I am going to write a book some day, called *Radiant Fatherhood*, which will make the whole thing seem beautiful and natural, and an experience to

be cherished for a lifetime (which is, indeed, as long as one can cherish anything).

Samuel Marchbanks' first book was published in 1947; it wasn't *Radiant Fatherhood*, it was *The Diary of Samuel Marchbanks*. His second was *The Tabletalk of Samuel Marchbanks* in 1949. This *Almanack* is Marchbanks' third book; it also is the eighteenth book by Robertson Davies. And that faces us with a problem that has troubled some thoughtful readers: what is the relation of Samuel Marchbanks to Robertson Davies? It is a symbiotic relation, a complex one. Robertson Davies is Samuel Marchbanks, but Samuel Marchbanks is not Robertson Davies. If that seems less than clear, perhaps it can be clarified by tracing here the careers of both Davies and Marchbanks.

Robertson Davies scented printer's ink very soon after he was born in the village of Thamesville, in South-Western Ontario, in 1913, under the sign of Virgo. His father, Rupert Davies, had come from Wales at fifteen and had learned the printing trade in Brantford. His first paper, which he owned, wrote, and printed himself, was the Thamesville *Herald*. When Mr. Davies took over the Renfrew *Mercury* in 1919, that small town near the Ottawa River became to Robertson Davies what Hannibal was to Samuel Clemens. In Renfrew he received his schooling, as much out of, as in, an Ontario little red schoolhouse. He continued high school in Kingston when his father bought the Kingston *British Whig* (later *Whig-Standard*), and finished his pre-University years at Upper Canada College, where he was editor of the college paper. From Queen's University in Kingston he went on to three years of reading English at Balliol and to a vigorous involvement in the Oxford University Dramatic Society. In 1939 he published his first book, a scholarly study, *Shakespeare's Boy Actors*. In the same year he joined the Old Vic Company in London as an actor of minor parts and as instructor in the History of the Drama in the Old Vic Theatre School. At the Old Vic he met the Australian stage manager, Brenda Mathews. They were married after the Company suspended production in the early months of the War. He was rejected for military service, and they moved to Canada in 1940.

After a year and a half of apprenticeship under one of Canada's finest journalists, B. K. Sandwell, on the Toronto *Saturday Night*, Davies became editor of the Peterborough *Examiner*.

Peterborough in 1942 was a small Ontario city of some 25,000, centre of a large farming area on the southern edge of the almost unbroken woods and lake country of the Laurentian Shield. Although life in Peterborough was somewhat disheveled by the War, it was not unlike life in Kingston, without Kingston's University, Penitentiary, Royal Military College, Insane Asylum, and Older Families. Peterborough factories were busy with War work; most of the younger people were away in the Services, and the men in the Army Basic Training Camp in the south end of town came and went too quickly to become part of town life. Gasoline was rationed. The nearest city with theatres, music, and bookstores was that Ontario Athens of the North, Toronto, eighty miles south-west by CPR.

In Ontario communities like Peterborough, the Editor of the local newspaper was accorded a high place, along with doctors, the Judge, clergymen, older established lawyers, Members of Parliament, and the heads of large industries (mostly Americans). Davies had to win this accord, for he was young, an outsider, and had a beard. He won it, by making what had been a good local paper a better local paper and a more cosmopolitan one. His editorials were unusually well-informed, liberal, vigorous, and independent in view, and were incisively written. During the twenty years of his editorship, the *Examiner* became one of the most widely quoted newspapers in Canada; it was handsomely redesigned and printed; its circulation doubled from under 13,000 to over 26,000.

The *Examiner* was understaffed in those War years, and Davies wrote not only the daily editorials and a twice-weekly book review column of high literary quality, but also reported cultural events about town. The name "Samuel Marchbanks" (derived from the Christian name and the surname of two of his grandfathers) was first the byline of the book review column. But starting on Saturday, November 13, 1943, a new weekly column appeared on the editorial page, entitled "The Diary of Samuel Marchbanks." In it, Marchbanks emerged as a full-blooded character. Like Mrs. Elinor Roosevelt's popular "My Day," the "Diary" was a full-length weekly column, divided into seven parts, each headed by the name of a day of the week. It caught on; it was reprinted in several other papers, and it ran from 1943 to 1953, totalling finally some 3,500 entries.

Davies developed the "Diary" partly to entertain his *Examiner* readers, and partly to blow off steam. Daily newspaper work required him to hold in his strong dramatic instinct and exuberant imagination; moreover after Oxford, London, the Old Vic, and the *Saturday Night* editorial room, some of the pieties of a provincial Ontario town were galling.

He might have amused his readers by playing the professional "funny man," or the crackerbarrel philosopher, but that would not have eased his own internal pressures. Besides, he did not underrate the intelligence of his *Examiner* audience. What he created was a persona, Samuel Marchbanks. Marchbanks' feelings and opinions are those of Robertson Davies— selected, transmuted, and dramatized as a verbal performance.

The qualification is important, for a wide range of Davies' own experience never appeared in the column. The Tuesday paragraph quoted at the beginning of this "Introduction" shows how the minutiae of actual experience was transformed. Some Peterborough people thought they recognized themselves in characters harpooned by Marchbanks; they were wrong, for Davies did not satirize or celebrate individuals.

Marchbanks is unique in personality; nevertheless he is fundamentally a Peterborough Everyman. We can recognize Marchbanks in our neighbours (if we are fortunate in our neighbours), and they can recognize him in us (if they also are fortunate). In his fantasies we recognize what goes on so often much closer to home. Technically, Marchbanks is brother to the "Y" of Stephen Leacock's "My Financial Career," and cousin to Samuel Clemens' persona, Mark Twain. Marchbanks' sharp eye, quirky individuality, and sonorous, witty speech also reflect Davies' delight in the matter and manner of many other writers: Pepys, Aubrey, Anthony à Wood, Robert Burton; in the King James Version; in Shakespeare and Jonson; in George Bernard Shaw, Logan Pearsall Smith, and H. L. Mencken.

In 1947, Davies selected 365 entries from the "Diary" columns, ordered them to present a year's round, and had them published as *The Diary of Samuel Marchbanks*. This Marchbanks is even more clearly the centre of his domestic world of Marchbanks Towers. The book form of the "Diary" was popular, and in 1949 Davies made another selection from the accumulating columns, and published it as *The Tabletalk of Samuel Marchbanks*. The Marchbanks who speaks here is less the Man about the House, more the Urbane man talking over the dinner table, his own, and, more often, that of others. He talks brilliantly, as we often dream we ought to have talked after some social encounter where we remained slow-witted and tongue-tied.

Eighteen years unwound between Marchbanks' *Tabletalk* and his third book, this *Almanack*. Davies stopped writing the "Diary" column in 1953 because he was immersed in writing the plays, fiction, and literary criticism (along with editorial work and theatricals) which have led to his reputation as one of Canada's most talented writers. His first plays, the one-acters in *Eros at Breakfast and Other Plays*, and the full-length *Fortune My Foe*, were published in 1949, followed by *At My Heart's Core* and five others. The early plays have been produced frequently; several won awards in the Dominion Drama Festival, and *Eros* was played in Edinburgh during that Festival. Davies also was active in the establishment of the Stratford Shakespeare Festival, and wrote three books, with Sir Tyrone Guthrie, on the first three seasons. Another major part of his work includes three novels of Salterton life, *Tempest Tost*,

Leaven of Malice, and *A Mixture of Frailties. Leaven of Malice* was produced in dramatic form as *Love and Malice* by Sir Tyrone Guthrie in 1960. During these years he also carried on regular book review columns in the *Saturday Night* and "A Writer's Diary" in the Toronto *Star* and other papers. Alfred Knopf asked him to assemble a volume of his criticism; it appeared in 1960 as *A Voice from the Attic.* Dramatic, literary, and academic awards were bestowed on him. In 1960 he also took up his long-suspended academic career when Trinity College appointed him Visiting Professor of English. He left the *Examiner* in 1963 to help plan Massey College, a residential graduate college in the University of Toronto. He now is Master of Massey College, and professor of English drama in the graduate school of the University.

Marchbanks did not die in 1953. Recently paperback editions of the *Diary* and the *Tabletalk* have been published, in which some passages worn by time have been replaced by new passages. And now this *Almanack.* Like the *Diary* and *Tabletalk,* it has its own principle of selection and organization. It too follows an old popular literary pattern, for almanacks have been produced since the time of Ptolemies. Almanacks describe primarily the progress of the astronomical or astrological year, and have been laced with information about things agricultural, medicinal, social, gastronomical, and what not. Some have been comic; others full of tall tales; others full of wise-saws and worldly advice. Marchbanks' is a miscellany. Many of the entries have been selected from *Examiner* columns of the late 40's and early 50's where Marchbanks expanded his range beyond that of the earlier columns. Others have been written more recently, and reflect experience amid the poison ivy and other undergrowth in the Groves of Academe. Like the *Diary* and the *Tabletalk,* this book is best savoured if read in small doses.

The title "Wizard" before Marchbanks' name should not puzzle many readers. A Wizard is a man with unusual knowledge of the human heart and the power of insight into the future. There are still wizards in Wales; in North America they are called by other names: doctor, professor, advertising or marketing consultant, psychiatrist, artist or writer. Nowadays many of them use computors, or simulate computors. Marchbanks scorns mechanical aids. His wizardry lies in his horse-sense, his humanism, and his wit and candour; his power lies in his language.

*

GORDON ROPER.

Trinity College, in the
University of Toronto.

PREFACE,

WHICH IT IS UNWISE

TO SKIP

IF YOU ARE LOOKING for an ordinary Almanac, containing information about the tides, postal rates, public holidays and the like, this is not the book for you. What I offer in these pages is a miscellany which may serve a variety of purposes, but the imparting of commonplace facts is not one of them. The themes of my book are Astrological and Inspirational.

The *Almanack* is divided into twelve sections which correspond to the signs of the Zodiac. At the beginning of each section a valuable Character Analysis will be found, compiled by Wizard Marchbanks. The special quality of these analyses is their utter frankness. There are scores of other astrological books on the market that attempt to soften the message of the stars. I have scorned subterfuge, which has done so much to bring astrology into disrepute. The twelve character analyses also permit the *Almanack* to be used as a Birthday Book, and a key to the nature of anyone you can persuade to entrust you with the date of their birth.

A word of warning: if you were born at a date which is within the last four days of any zodiacal period, or within the first three days of one, you are in an astrological mess called a "cusp," and you partake of the characteristics of both the signs under which you were born. If you were born, let us say, on August 22nd, you are influenced by both Leo and Virgo;

you are leonine and virginal in equal measure – a vexing predicament for you and all who know you. This confusion of temperament among those born in cusps has given rise to the astrological expression "a queer cusp" to describe such a person.

The Inspirational material in the *Almanack* is drawn from my private papers – Diaries, Commonplace Books, Soul Scrapings and accumulated Correspondence and Letter Files. Though no special coherence is attempted in the arrangement of this material I hope that these random recollections and revelations by myself and my friends may permit the reader to dip into the book at any point, and find some Sweetly Solemn Thought, suitable for reflection or Solace in a Dark Hour.

As a boy I spent many happy hours poring over a series of books bearing such titles as *A Day With Walter Scott*, and *A Day With Tennyson*. I have felt for some time that the moment was near to offer the public *A Day With Marchbanks*, but as you, my readers, have been most generous toward me in the past I am unwilling to hold you down to one measly day; it would ill become me to play the niggard in offering you these riches of the spirit.

*

SAMUEL MARCHBANKS.

from the Horoscope-Casting Chamber
Marchbanks Towers.

Minerva Hauser b. April 1, 1876
during the Great Frost

Aries ♈

♂ Mars

a fiery sign

(March 22 to April 20)

ARIES IS the sign of the Ram, and those born under it are of robust physical health, strongly dominating disposition and destined to be leaders. If you are not a leader now, explain this to your friends and employers, and show them that, if you are to make fullest use of your powers, you must be given your own way in everything. Once you have made this important adjustment to fate, you should enjoy a life of considerable happiness. Do not worry that you are not strongly intellectual; instinct is your best friend and you should never hesitate to act upon it, even when others counsel caution. People born under your sign often die violent deaths, so choose your friends carefully, and always look under the bed before retiring. Your sex-life may cause remark among the jealous: frown them down.

1 ✳

According to the best astrological authorities, your lucky colours are red, white and blue; your flowers are the anemone, the hawthorn and the buttercup; your stones are the beryl, the green jasper, the coral, carnelian, amethyst, sapphire and diamond. You may easily deal with the matter of colours by keeping a small Union Jack or Stars and Stripes tucked in your pocket; the Canadian flag isn't lucky enough for you. I admit that all your lucky flowers are difficult to make into any sort of presentable bouquet, and you have to be especially careful with hawthorn, which flowers for a week or so in June, but carries thorns as long as horseshoe nails for twelve months of the year. Of your lucky stones, the diamond is easily the most popular, and any suggestion that your engagement ring should contain a piece of green jasper instead of the brighter stone should be dealt with firmly. The amethyst, by the way, is said to be a safeguard against drunkenness, but do not test this to the uttermost; you may require a larger amethyst than you can conveniently afford.

*

Health Hints for Those Born Under Aries

Your weak points, astrologers agree, are your stomach and kidneys, and, to be frank, two more inconvenient places to conk out could hardly be imagined. Your best plan, perhaps, is to eat and drink all you can while your stomach and kidneys are still working and then, when they give up, you will at least have the wistful fun of poring over old menus. There are those who recommend great moderation in diet from earliest childhood, but if you investigate the personal history of those who give such counsel you will usually find that they were born under a strong-gizzarded planet, and eat and drink like refugees. Moderation in eating and drinking is to be avoided for as long as possible, as it is a great vexation while it is going on, and disposes you to regretful recollections when you are living on crackers and boiled milk. The kidneys, by the way, may be fortified by drinking rain water which has run off a tarred roof; the creosote in the water provides the organs with a useful extra lining which will resist virtually anything. Drink molten rubber, also, but never to excess; melted party balloons serve very well.

*

MEDITATIONS AT RANDOM

NAÏVETÉ OF CANADIAN FOXES / Was talking to one of the few people in Canada who hunts foxes on a horse, and with hounds, in the English fashion. It is not generally known that there is a small but persistent survival of the fox-hunt in this country. But this man told me that Canadian foxes are either stupider than English foxes, or do not realize what is expected of them; the last fox he hunted, he said, ran in a circle of about a hundred yards, rushing directly at the hounds, who ate it as best they could while rolling around on the ground, holding their sides and laughing in their rich, doggy voices. Because of this lack of gumption among foxes, it is usual to drag a sack of some strong-smelling stuff over a good long course, and let the hounds follow that. The question which occurs to me is: would there be any money in training foxes for this highly specialized work? It would be wearing for a man of my temperament to drag a fox on a rope through streams, in and out of holes, and over ploughed fields, but I am willing to try it if I can thereafter rent the fox to hunters at a stiff fee. If they kill my trained fox, of course, I shall expect to be pensioned for life.

WHOSE NEWS IS GOOD NEWS? / Travelling by train, I found that across the aisle from me were some English businessmen, new to Canada and apparently here to reap some dollars for the home-land. They had a lot of Canadian newspapers with them, and they expressed their dislike of these loudly and with great frank-ness. "Rags" was the most flattering word they employed, and they agreed that on the whole the papers were "simply Death." Even so I have heard Canadians blather their dislike of the English press, because the *Times* carried no account of the ploughing-match at Tin Cup (B.C.); I suppose these Englishmen missed news of the Harvest Festival at Lesser Piddle-in-Puddle (Beds). English papers publish very little Canadian news and Englishmen are apt to snigger in a superior manner when this is pointed out to them; they imply that Canada has no news that anybody wants to hear. So I was glad that these noisy rascals found our papers distasteful for identical reasons, and I read my own sheet with loud "Oohs" ánd "Ahs" indicative of extreme relish, to vex them. And it did, and they moved to the dining-car, grumbling at the thought of being given ice-water to drink.

NATIONAL CHARACTERISTICS / Attended a theatrical performance and was impressed once again by the amount of coughing which a Canadian assembly can manage, and by the freedom with which this national habit is indulged. Not merely the aged and infirm, but the young and the hearty, the valiant and the fair, cut loose with coughs like the roaring of lions. Mentally ran off a new verse for our national song, thus:

O Canada, our home, our native land,
Chronic catarrh makes all our tubes expand;
   With raucous cough we greet the dawn,
   With snorts we hail the noon,
   The emblems of our nation are
   The kerchief and spittoon;
      Post-nasal drip!
      Woooof! Let her rip!
We face the future trusting in our grippe –
(Exultantly and accompanied with loud coughs, hawkings, gaggings and retchings.)
DE-FY The World with Freedom in OUR GRIPPE!

*

FROM MY FILES

To Samuel Marchbanks, ESQ.

Dear Mr. Marchbanks:

    I hear that you are going on a trip abroad, and that you are going by plane. Of course I wish you the best of luck but I suppose you have been reading the papers lately? These plane accidents are the limit, aren't they? Every day a plane or two seems to crash somewhere. This being so, will you be wanting your garden hose if anything should happen? I mean you won't, of course, but what I mean is can I have it? We have never been very close friends, but I would like something to remember you by, and mine is going all to pieces.

    Bon voyage and happy landings,
      Dick Dandiprat.

*

To Richard Dandiprat, ESQ.

My good Dandiprat:

    No, you may not have my garden hose under any circumstances. If evil should befall me while in flight, it will become the property of my heirs. They will, I presume, have to water the grass just as if I were alive. Your attitude suggests that of the vulture.

    Indignantly,
      Samuel Marchbanks.

*

To Samuel Marchbanks, ESQ.

Dear Mr. Marchbanks:

    I have received your request for something to keep you from being sick while flying. I confess that I have never had such a request before, but it is an interesting one, and I have spent some of my unengaged moments experimenting on a pill for you. I am sending you something which will deaden most of your nervous centres, and completely close your oesophagus, so you will be in no danger of throwing up, at any rate, ha, ha! I should be obliged if you would let me know how this pill works, and particularly if it has any unpleasant effect. I wish to perfect it, and any help you can give me will be appreciated. It is still in rather a rough state, and may be a little too powerful at present. Still, kill or cure. With good wishes for your voyage, I am,

      Raymond Cataplasm.

*

To Raymond Cataplasm, M.D., F.R.C.P.

Dear Dr. Cataplasm:

Thank you for the pills. You don't think they are rather big, do you? And don't you think black is rather an unsightly colour for a pill? You know best of course. However, as I wanted them for use while flying I experimented last night by giving one to a dog, and swinging it violently in a hammock. I am sorry to say that its oesophagus was not closed tight enough to prevent a very disagreeable outcome, and I had to get someone to do the cleaning up, as such incidents unnerve me. Furthermore, I was busy trying to revive the dog, who seemed to be in a coma, complicated by bad dreams. If you don't mind, I shall not take a whole pill if I feel unwell in the air; I shall merely lick one. To make this simpler I am mounting them on sticks, like lollipops.

      Sincerely,
      Samuel Marchbanks.

*

To Samuel Marchbanks, ESQ.

Dear Mr. Marchbanks:

Although it is some years since we met I am sure that you will remember me perfectly. I hear that you are going to Edinburgh by air, and I write at once to ask a small favour. Will you take my sewing-machine with you, and send it on to my sister in Aberdeen? For some years I have been looking for an opportunity to send it to her, but I would not trust it to unfriendly hands. The machine will reach you tomorrow. I know that you will not mind doing this, as I have read all your books in our Public Library.

      Yours sincerely,
      Minerva Hawser.

   *

To Miss Minerva Hawser.

Dear Miss Hawser:

I am returning your machine, which weighs 75 lbs., collect. I am only permitted 66 lbs. of baggage. Yours without regret,

S. Marchbanks.

*

To Amyas Pilgarlic, ESQ.

Dear Pil:

You have often complained that the art of correspondence is in decline, and I suppose you are right. Everything seems to be in decline, one way or another. The long eighteenth century letter is a thing of the past. I seem to spend a large part of each day writing notes of all sorts, though I rarely get a chance to write long budgets of news to my friends – among whom I am proud to number you, you frowsy old pedant. I shall send you a postcard from abroad. By the way, do you remember Min Hawser? I thought she was dead, but I had a note from her the other day – wanting something, as always. The longevity of nuisances is one of Nature's inexplicable jokes.

With warm good wishes,

Sam.

*

To Samuel Marchbanks, ESQ.

Dear Mr. Marchbanks:

As you are in Edinburgh I know you will not mind doing a favour for an old friend and well-wisher. My family, as you know, is Scottish and I have long wanted to honour the land of my forbears in some striking fashion. Will you buy, therefore, sixteen or eighteen yards of material in the Hawser Tartan – the Dress Hawser, not the Hunting Hawser – and bring it back to me when you come. You might as well see it through the Customs, to avoid any trouble. I shall then cause an evening dress to be made from it, which I shall wear on any occasion which seems to warrant such a display. I hope you enjoy your stay in "the land o' cakes."

Lang may your lum reek!

Minerva Hawser.

*

To Miss Minerva Hawser.

Dear Miss Hawser:

When I made enquiries here concerning the Hawser tartan I was greeted with oblique glances in several shops, and all knowledge of your family was hastily denied. Are you sure that you know all the circumstances which led to the migration of the Clan Hawser?

Long may your blood boil,
Samuel Marchbanks.

*

To Samuel Marchbanks, ESQ.

Dear Mr. Marchbanks:

As you are in Edinburgh I write to you for information on a matter which arouses me to anger. I read that the British, subverted by foreign *restaurateurs*, are now eating horseflesh. If this is true it must stop at once. Cruelty or indignity to dumb creatures is a thing I will not tolerate, even when it is post-humous. I demand that you get to the bottom of this story at once. And if you yourself have been eating any of our dumb friends, I command you, in the name of Canadian Womanhood, to desist immediately. Cows, yes; pigs, yes; fowl (so long as they are not singing birds) yes. Of cats I forbear to speak. But horses and dear, dear doggies – NO! Please reply immediately this reaches you. The eye of Canada is upon you.

Yours,
(MRS.) Kedijah Scissorbill.

*

To Mrs. Kedijah Scissorbill.

Dear Mrs. Scissorbill:

Pray compose yourself. I have not seen any horseflesh consumed as yet. If I have eaten it, I knew it not. Canada may therefore take its eye off me. I may perhaps quiet your suspicions regarding British Dogdom by telling you that there is a statue to a dog in Edinburgh; it is Greyfriars Bobbie, a dear doggie who used to go regularly with his master to a restaurant in Greyfriars; when his master died the doggie kept on going to the restaurant for 20 years, begging for food. Everyone was touched by this act of fidelity, including the restaurant-keeper, who reckoned that in that time Bobbie had sponged 7,300 meals from him which, at sixpence a time, amounted to a little over £180. He felt he had been extraordinarily touched. The statue of Bobbie was erected by American admirers of the dog. No other dog in history is known to have been faithful to one restaurant for so long. I am, Madam,

Your servant,
Samuel Marchbanks.

*

To Samuel Marchbanks, ESQ.

Dear Mr. Marchbanks:

What a disappointment about the tartan! Please try again. And another thing; I am anxious to possess some personal relic of Mary, Queen of Scots. Could you possibly get me something – one of her sweet little shoes, for instance. You must remember, Mr. Marchbanks, that I have been an orphan for the last 45 years. Surely I deserve some consideration from one who, whatever his faults, is a man, and should be glad to assist the weak and helpless.

Yours confidingly,
Minerva Hawser.

*

To Miss Minerva Hawser.

Dear Miss Hawser:

Really I cannot get the 18 yards of the Hawser tartan you ask for. Could you manage with an equal length of something else? I was talking two days ago with Mr. Telfer Dunbar, who is said to know more about tartans than anybody else in Edinburgh, and he says there is no earthly reason why anybody should not wear any tartan that pleases them. From my recollection of your person, a few yards of a hound's-tooth tweed suggests itself for an appropriate evening gown. As for Mary Queen of Scots' shoes, I have not seen any for sale. What makes you think, by the way, that they would be sweet and little? Are you aware that Mary was six feet tall? With such a physique she may well have had feet like a policeman. I fear that you are a romantic.

Yours unromantically,
Samuel Marchbanks.

*

To Amyas Pilgarlic, ESQ.

Dear Pil:

I am having a wonderful time in Edinburgh. There is a kindly spirit here which is beyond the professional kindliness of tourist bureaux; it is entirely genuine and unselfish. The Festival is the great thing at present, of course. There are a good many young people about, as well as the usual congregation of the lame, the halt and the blind that artistic gatherings always attract. There are plenty of Scots wearing the kilt, and last night I saw some of them dance a strathspey most attractively, and then follow it up with a dance called "Prince Charles of Edinburgh." I suggested that he was Prince of Wales, and attracted some darkling Highland glances. The Scots nationalists tend to wear beards as a sort of trademark, and from time to time I am mistaken for one of their number. There are all sorts of things here which would engage your scholarly attention: for instance, a learned Scot showed me a volume of poems by Burns which have not previously been collected, as they were deemed to be of too frank a nature to appear in print. Mild stuff, really, in the lurid light of modern literature but the Scots have a low threshold of outrage. And you would be delighted by the magnificent stone-masonry one sees everywhere, and by the high quality of commercial sign-writing even on the most ordinary shops. I saw one yesterday bearing the name of "Madam Doubtfire"; charming, don't you think? And I have seen a tram which claimed it went to Joppa. Surely odder even than a Streetcar named Desire?

> Yours,
> Sam.

*

To Samuel Marchbanks, ESQ.

Dear Marchbanks:

While you are in Scotland will you collect and send me a dozen new Scotch stories? I have just been appointed to head the Speaker's Committee of the Rowanis Club for the next year, and good funny stories are scarce. I find that stories about Scotchmen are always popular. Oh, yes, and will you send me a few tips about the Scotch accent? Everybody thinks I tell stories very well, but I have only one funny accent and it has to do for Scotch, Irish, Jewish, Negro, etc. I would like to specialize in Scotch stories. Please hurry about this, as I haven't any time to waste.

> Yours eagerly,
> Dick Dandiprat.

*

To Richard Dandiprat, ESQ.

My presumptuous Dandiprat:

I have no time to send you Scotch stories, even if I knew any. Nor can I help you with your assault upon Scottish vernacular. Everyone speaks it here, but it defies analysis. Yesterday a lady of my acquaintance said to me, "Hoo lang is it sin' ye pit meat in yer wame?" She was enquiring when I had last eaten. The acquisition of the right accent for such a remark is far beyond your feeble powers so no more from

> Yours regretfully,
> S. Marchbanks.

*

To Amyas Pilgarlic, ESQ.

Dear Pil:

At last the flood of letters subsides, and I have a moment to write to you.

The Edinburgh-London journey took from 10:40 a.m. until 8:15 p.m. I grew bored with sitting still and felt like the Hermit in the legend. You know it? It seems that there dwelt in the desert a certain Hermit whose goodness and austerity were so great that news of him reached the ears of the Patriarch of Jerusalem. So the Patriarch sent for the Hermit, who bestrode a mule and rode without stopping for 40 days and 40 nights. At last he was in the presence of the Patriarch, who considerately bade him to take a seat. "Nay," said the Hermit, "of sitting, as of all earthly pleasures, there cometh at length satiety."

Meals in English trains are perhaps a little worse than they used to be. That brown soup is somewhat browner, the coffee is somewhat weaker, and the cheese hints more strongly than ever at an origin in a soap factory. The English are not really a puritanical people, but railway meals suggest a dreadful mortification of the flesh – an urge to take the joy out of travel.

As I wander about my fancy is greatly caught by the unusual names which I see on signs and advertisements. Just as I left Edinburgh I saw a beauty over a clothing store – Clinkscales. Now if I wrote a book in which anyone was called Clinkscales the critics would accuse me of being fanciful. Yet it appears that people of that name really exist. Wonderful! Travel is so broadening.

Yours broadly,
Sam.

*

To Samuel Mockbanks, ESQ.

Dear Mr. Mackbonks:

In your correspondence with the Passport Agency and Fiscal Control Board recently, your "Form Z" was returned to this office unstamped. It is therefore invalid, and the sterling currency now in your possession has no legal existence. In order that your position may be regularized as soon as possible, you must secure Forms H and Q from the British Currency Legitimization Authority, and obtain permission to export one cent (1¢) in Canadian currency to us. We shall purchase a one-cent stamp for your "Form Z" with this sum. A further charge for service in purchasing, moistening and affixing the stamp, amounting to five dollars, will also be charged. Please attend to this matter immediately, as until you do so your money is a fiction.

Yours,
     Haubergeon Hydra
     (Sub-deputy Fiscal Repressor).

*

To Haubergeon Hydra, ESQ.

Dear Mr. Hydra:

Far be it from me to dispute the word of a government official, but my sterling currency seems to be quite real. The people of Edinburgh are willing and even eager to accept it. However, if you want a one-cent stamp I happen, by a lucky chance, to have one in my pocket, which I enclose. You overestimate the difficulty of getting it on to the document; it is not five dollars worth of work even for a Civil Servant. Just a quick lick and a slap, and it's done.

Yours, with dripping tongue,
     Samuel Marchbanks.

*

To Miss Minerva Hawser.

Dear Miss Hawser:

Yes, I quite understand your passion for relics of eminent persons. But I assure you, dear lady, that it is not easy for me to procure for you anything which would be, as you phrase it in your letter to me "a link with past greatness, and an inspiration to great achievement." You have asked me for Sir Walter Scott's walking-stick and for Robert Burns' snuffbox; I regret that both of these interesting objects are in museums, and I am too timid to steal them, even in order that you may exhibit them to the Canadian Authors' Association, who doubtless need them.

The only relic I can get you is associated with Haigh, the Vampire; no doubt you read that he was hanged on August 10, 1949, for murdering no less than nine ladies of about your own age and general character; after each murder he drank a glass of his victim's blood, mingled with a liquid which he supplied from his own person. How's that for connoisseurship? A friend of mine has a tumbler which he is practically certain was used by Haigh in one of those curious toasts, and he will let me have it for only £10. If you want it please cable this sum immediately. I am sure your branch of the Authors' Association would be thrilled. All friends around the punchbowl!

Yours amiably,
     Samuel Marchbanks.

*

To Haubergeon Hydra, ESQ.

Dear Mr. Hydra:

As I understand that you are permanent secretary of the Government Alcoholic Discouragement Board, I write to ask you why there is no cider for sale in my part of Canada. Since coming to Britain I have renewed my acquaintance with this wonderful drink (or beverage, as I suppose you call it) and I want to know why I cannot get it at home. Canada is a great apple country: then why no cider? Cider rejoiceth the heart of man (and of woman) Hydra, old boy, and the Canadian heart could do with a good rejoicing.

A brand of cider which I particularly like is sold here under the brand name of "Woodpecker." I think this must be because the explosion of the bubbles in the throat and stomach of the drinker is exactly as though some jolly woodpecker had crept in there and was pecking happily away, right, left and centre.

Yours merrily,

Samuel Marchbanks.

*

To Samuel Marblinks, ESQ.

Dear Mrs. Matblanks:

Your letter re cider to hand and contents noted. In reply would beg to state that (a) the Civil Service cannot entertain suggestions from unofficial sources and (b) cider is objectionable to the Medical Association, the apple being a notorious Physician Repellent, and a prominent feature in the coat-of-arms of the Royal College of Chiropractic Healers.

Yours semi-officially,

Haubergeon Hydra.

for Government Alcoholic Discouragement Board.

*

To Mrs. Kedijah Scissorbill.

Dear Mrs. Scissorbill:

As you wished it, I visited the National Portrait Gallery and verified your suspicion that it contains no portrait of the Canadian heroine, Laura Secord. I made enquiries about this and was told by a person in authority that only portraits of eminent persons who have lived in the British Isles were sought for the Gallery; obviously this is a mere excuse. The truth is, the British are jealous of Laura Secord, and want to belittle her.

I feel that while I am on this subject I should tell you of an ugly rumour I heard yesterday from a fellow-Canadian; he said that the famous portrait of Laura Secord was really a picture of an early and obscure premier of Ontario, upon whom a bonnet had been painted. You had better take this up with your women's club, and kill the rumour before it runs across Canada like wildfire, destroying the national pride of little children.

Yours agitatedly,
S. Marchbanks.

*

To *Raymond Cataplasm*, M.D., F.R.C.P.

Dear Dr. Cataplasm:

Do you want to make a fortune? Convince the Canadian people that they need another meal. Already Canadians are addicts of the English custom of morning coffee: convince them that they need afternoon tea and you will be hailed as a medical genius equal with Dr. Abernethy (who invented a biscuit) and Dr. Graham (who invented a new kind of bread).

Canada has a vast sweet tooth. Think of the oceans of pop, the glaciers of ice-cream, the deluges of milk-shakes, and the tons of chocolates that we descendants of the hardy pioneers consume every year. You have but to persuade the Canadians that they need a meal consisting of rich pastries every afternoon at four, and your reputation is made! Tell them that their efficiency sags at four, and that they need food to stave off heart failure, and the rest will be easy. The road to a nation's pocketbook is through its stomach; don't tell anybody else.

I offer this suggestion quite without strings, of course, if you choose to knock anything off my next bill, that is entirely your affair.

Your perennial patient,
S. Marchbanks.

*

To *Haubergeon Hydra*, ESQ.

Dear Hydra:

As a civil servant you are undoubtedly interested in new categories of human beings, so I write to tell you of one which came my way yesterday, when I stopped for a drink at the Hop Pole Inn, in Tewkesbury, with my uncle Fortunatus. We had been travelling, as had another man who entered the bar just before us: he wandered disconsolately to the far end of the room, and shortly returned looking more woeful than before. "Gents?" said Uncle Fortunatus, helpfully: "No, only Ladies and Telephones," said the man, and disappeared toward the street.

Yours,
Samuel Marchbanks.

*

To Mrs. Morrigan.

My very dear Mrs. Morrigan:

Knowing how fond you have always been of gypsies, I write to tell you that yesterday I saw a tribe of them converging on the ancient and beautiful Shropshire town of Ludlow. As I drove along the road from Wales to Ludlow I passed ten gypsy caravans – surely the most romantic dwellings in the world, shining with brass ornaments, and gay with shawls, quilts and bits of tinsel. Every caravan horse was led by a man, usually an old rascal, but sometimes a handsome, black-eyed lad: in front of the van would be a young woman, nursing a baby; in the back of the van other children tumbled, dirty, fat and lively. The women were all either young beauties or old hags: are there no middle-aged women among gypsies? And how the beauty of a gypsy woman surpasses that of the simpering lollipops of the films! How wondrously they dress, and how they make even their very dirt become them!

A few days ago I was passing through the Welsh hamlet of Penegoes, where Richard Wilson was born. A group of gypsy children were playing around a fire there, outside a queer tent made of skins, and obviously half as old as time. How Wilson could have painted them! Do you suppose that he would have agreed with Augustus John that, "it is always worth half-a-crown to have a good look at a gypsy – front or back view"? I accepted the invitation of a gypsy girl to touch her baby for luck. One shilling. Cheap at double the money.

Your humble servant,
Samuel Marchbanks.

*

To the Rev. Simon Goaste, B.D.

Dear Mr. Goaste:

I am sorry to hear that your thrombosis has been at you again. You should come to North Wales. There is no thrombosis here – at least, not under that name. There is a similar affliction, but it moves in three stages. The first of these, usually marked by a coma lasting a few hours, is called a "warning." The next, which usually involves partial paralysis, is called a "seizure." The final stage of the ailment is called a "stroke." I was looking at my great-grandfather's grave the other day, and the message on the headstone was: "Behold I shall take away the desire of thine eyes with a stroke." And that is precisely how my great-grandfather died.

But the usual age for demise here is in the 90's. It is an uncommonly healthy part of the world. The mountain air, I suppose.

Your obedient parishioner,
  S. Marchbanks.

*

FROM MY NOTEBOOKS

A RIVAL ALMANACK / An almanac from a patent medicine company arrived in the mail this morning – a gaudy reminder of the immense tonnage of pills, the vast ocean of jalap, the heaped-up mountains of salts which are consumed by the Canadian public every year. Not that I have any prejudice against patent medicines. They are a relatively harmless indulgence and may even contribute to human well-being. It does a man good to take a few pills every day. It gives him a feeling that he is taking care of himself, and this persuades him that he is in good health – but only just. It is not advisable to feel too well. People who boast about their good health are apt to overtax it. They want to lift things which should be left on the ground; they insist upon walking when it would be much simpler to ride. Everybody should have some slight, not too obtrusive ailment, which he coddles. Nobody should be without some harmless medicine which he takes. These things enable him to husband his strength, harbour his resources, and live to a ripe old age. And, what is more, the patent medicine people, who are a good and useful social group upon the whole, must live.

LAUGHABLE NUDITY / This evening some worldly acquaintance took me to a nightclub, where I watched the floor-show with simple-minded wonder. One of the chief attractions was a blonde young woman, said to be Finnish, who danced in an Eastern costume that afforded her strategic but not complete protection. She was less graceful than supple, and when she had got her feet very dirty she showed us how she could waggle them over her shoulders. Then she turned herself into a wheel of irregular contour and rolled lumpily about the floor. Her abdomen was rubbery and less taut than many I have seen, and every time she fell on it there was an audible and rather comical Splat! which amused me greatly. However, I was frowned on for laughing. In Toronto, it appears, one may leer desirously at under-dressed girls, or gape at them with the costive expression of one who considers Nudity and Art to be synonymous terms, but one must not laugh. Which is unreasonable, considering that many people are even funnier stripped than clothed.

ILLUSION OF PROGRESS / A child showed me a comic book that sought to show how much better life is today than it was in the 18th century. It pointed out rather smugly that in those days there was no electricity, that many people could not read, and that life was somewhat inconvenient. So far as I am concerned life is still far from convenient, but pleasant for all that, and many people who can read do not seem to do so. Further, some things achieved a perfection in the 18th century which has never since been surpassed: we have never bettered their window-sashes, for instance; nor have we designed any chairs which combine beauty and comfort as theirs did; our glass and china-ware are not, on the whole, as good as theirs, nor are our textiles. In fact, in virtually every phase of architecture and industrial design, they beat the heads off us and we still copy them because we cannot do better. It is dishonest to give children the notion that we are cleverer than our ancestors in every respect. We make many things more easily than they, but not necessarily better.

AGREEMENT WITH SATAN / A lady writes to me, unreasonably angry because I have let it be known that I dwelt within myself and peeped out at the world. "I know the kind of man you are," she writes; "you are the kind who would agree with the lines –

The mind is its own place, and in itself
Can make a heaven of hell, a hell of heaven.

And do you know who said that?" Yes, my dear madam, I know who said that: it was Satan, in *Paradise Lost*. And a remarkably intelligent and able fellow he was, too, and quite the best character Milton ever created. . . . But I make no such vast claims for myself; I can make a hell of heaven but the other trick is too much for me.

VICTIM OF SCIENTIFIC COMFORT / Woke feeling like a piece of pemmican; my electric blanket had dried me out during the night. Two years ago a kind friend gave me this luxury, and I owe many a snug night to it, but from time to time I curse its remorseless efficiency. If it is cold when I go to bed I push the controller on the blanket up as high as it will go, and compose myself for slumber with a smile, knowing that nothing short of a new Ice Age can harm me. But sometimes the temperature changes sharply in the night, and after dreams that I am lost in the desert, where my dromedary has dropped dead from thirst, I awaken to find that it is thawing outside, and that I am in danger of bursting into flames. I then drag myself to the bath-room, fill the tub with water, and leap into it. There is a sizzle and a suck, and all the water has disappeared, but I am back to my normal size and wetness, and feel much better. But one of these times I shall not wake, and the cinder which will comprise my mortal remains will be buried in a pillbox.

*

CULLED FROM THE APOPHTHEGMS
OF WIZARD MARCHBANKS

Beware of an optimism founded on superficial judgements: otherwise you will dismiss Death as Nature's bounty toward the undertaking industry.

Waghorn Wittol.
b. May 1, 1920
but during a
total eclipse.

Taurus

Venus!

a fixed, very earthy sign

(April 21 to May 21)

TAURUS IS the sign of the Bull and those born under it should be of a powerful physique; if this is not so in your case, you should consult your physician, or ascertain if you have not been deceived about the date of your birth. You are of a lovably violent disposition, but those who have won your confidence can lead you by the nose. You would do well to have your voice trained, for many of the most admired singers were born under this sign. You are fortunate, if not subtle, in affairs of the heart, and you have a tendency to be fickle. Women born under Taurus are of a placid and gentle disposition, massive in physique, profoundly maternal and untroubled by intellectual conflict. The digestion of Taurians of both sexes is admirable, but they should beware of diseases of the foot or the mouth, which may be serious. You are, upon the whole, earthy, and in the present state of literature you could hardly do better than to try your hand at authorship.

✳ 18

Enchantment-of-the-Month

✻✛✺✛✻✛✺✛✻✛✺✛✻✛✺✛✻✛✺✛

Your lucky colours for dress and household decoration are pale blue, indigo, lemon yellow, black, dark brown and leaden gray. I know that this is terrible, but you can't be lucky and becomingly dressed at the same time, so you had better make your choice. Your flowers are not much better; they are the trailing arbutus, the violet, hyacinth, daisy, cowslip and jonquil. Your stones are the moonstone, the opal, beryl, carnelian, sapphire and chrysolite. If you insist upon being lucky, I suggest that you adopt some profession which permits you to do your work entirely naked; failing that, you might confine your lucky colours to your undergarments, and do the best you can without flowers. Of your lucky stones the sapphire is unquestionably the luckiest, and if you achieve a good one, you will be so lucky that you might tempt fate in the matter of colour.

Health Hints for Those Born Under Taurus

You are very strong, except for possible weakness of the throat. You can minimize this danger by keeping your mouth shut. Because of the Bull strain in your astrological makeup, nobody will take it amiss if you breathe somewhat forcibly through your nose; it may even be taken for a sign of strong character. Male Taurians are advised to wear high collars, preferably starched; female Taurians should lay in a supply of scarves and fur neckpieces. Your lucky fur is mink, but do not for this reason refuse even luckier furs, such as sable.

MEDITATIONS AT RANDOM

DR. SHAKESPEARE / Received a curious pamphlet from a doctor in West Virginia; it was a reprint of a speech he made before the Section on Diseases of the Chest at the 99th Session of the American Medical Association in 1950, and is called "Shakespeare's Knowledge of Chest Diseases." In this strange work the good physician proves that Shakespeare knew that people had lungs, because he mentions them nineteen times. He also knew that there was such a thing as consumption and asthma, and one of his heroines (Beatrice in *Much Ado About Nothing*) suffers from a cold in the head, so we must assume that Shakespeare knew that there was such a disease as a cold. All this seems to amaze the West Virginian doctor, and suggests to him that Shakespeare was a pretty smart fellow. But I can take this information calmly. Though I am no Shakespeare, I have long been acquainted with all these facts myself. People who are not poets are often astonished to find that poets know anything at all; they seem to think that poets are born stupid, and get worse as they grow older. But I have long recognized the fact that true poets are among the very few sane people in a mad world.

A FORGOTTEN COMPOSER / Looking through a song-book in a friend's house today I came upon a ballad which was a great favourite with contraltos in my childhood; it was *Three Fishers* by John Pyke Hullah, with words by the Rev. Charles Kingsley. The moaning of the harbour bar in the song was trifling compared with the moaning of the large, hollow-voiced women who sang it at church concerts and "musical evenings." Hullah was an odd man, who thought that he could devise an easier way of putting music on paper than the usual system of notes. He also composed an opera for which Charles Dickens wrote the libretto, a work which seems to have disappeared completely. That would be a curiosity, indeed, if it could be found. Hullah was the composer of *O That We Two Were Maying*, another favourite of my childhood, usually sung as a duet by a slate-pencil soprano and a fog-horn contralto; the audience always concurred heartily in their wish to be elsewhere.

VICTIM OF THE WEED / I was in conversation with a merry fellow who knew many odd scraps of history and told me that William McKinley, 25th President of the USA, died of a tobacco heart. "Surely he was assassinated by the anarchist, Leon Czolgosz?" said I. "Czolgosz shot him," said he, "but McKinley lingered for some time, and when he died several papers of strong moral tendency said that if his heart had not been weakened by tobacco smoking, he would have pulled through. I was alive then, and I recall it well; you can't imagine how powerful the anti-tobacco faction was in 1901." He also told me that the name of the killer was pronounced Cholguss, and many wits at the time said he had been driven to madness, and his rash act, by a lifetime of hearing it mispronounced.

*

FROM MY ARCHIVES

To Samuel Marchbanks, ESQ.

Dear Marchbanks:

I am offering you $50, cash down, for your car. It is a good make, only two years old, has first-class tires and has plainly been well cared for. That is why I am offering you $50, instead of the $25 which is what a dealer would give you.

The fact is that Chanel, that skunk that has been hanging around Marchbanks Towers for years, has been living in the garage since you went away. It looks as though she had made a nest in the back seat, and last night she was badly frightened by my dog, Bowser, who happened to be snooping around.

Take it or leave it. $50. I say nothing of the shock to Bowser's nerves, as you are a neighbour and I want to treat you decently.

Yours decently,
Dick Dandiprat.

*

To Samuel Marchbanks, ESQ.

Dear Mr. Marchbanks:

It occurs to me that now that you are in London you might look up some relatives of mine, the Mawworms. I have never met them myself, but in 1856 a half-sister of my grandmother, a Miss Eulalia Hawser, married Edmund Mawworm, who was considered to be a great catch. Since my family came to Canada, in 1888, the Hawsers and the Mawworms have rather lost touch, and I am anxious to renew the connection. I have a pair of gentlemen's military brushes, upon the backs of which the Mawworm crest is engraved; unfortunately the bristles are quite worn away.

You will be able to find their address easily, I am sure, as they used to be very well-known people, and had a large house somewhere in London, or quite near. Do call on them and suggest that I would be most happy to write. I am sure they will be interested.

Yours expectantly,
Minerva Hawser.

P.S. All the Mawworms have dark hair and I believe one of them is titled. If you find them will you cable their address to me at once.   M.H.

*

To Amyas Pilgarlic, ESQ.

Dear Pil:

It is high time I came home. Dandiprat and his dog have sabotaged my car and that accursed old crone, Min Hawser, is hounding me to run down relatives of hers who have titles. I cannot write to them now, as I am on a train bound for Wales, and you are the only one who can read my train-writing.

Railway travel in this country has one great advantage over train journeys in Canada; I can get unlimited reading matter in every station. There is a book-and-paper stand on every platform, offering the most delightful train literature. At present I have *The Matrimonial Post*, and *The Girl's Own Paper* with me. Have you read either? They are very rich feeding, let me tell you. Consider this, from the *Post*: "Attractive, witty, physically opulent lady of modest means seeks correspondence with gentleman of refined but not inhibited mentality. Object, a mutual exploration of intellect, with a view to intimacy and possibly matrimony. Photograph offered and expected." Or how does this appeal to you: "Lady, 28, who has lost one leg, seeks congenial gentleman friend with similar handicap. Friendship and possible matrimony." Or what do you say to this choice offer: "Gentleman, mature but well-preserved, amusing, presentable, experienced, seeks ditto lady with private means. Offers unlimited comradeship and fun." I can dream over the *Post* for hours, calling up the opulent ladies and comradely gentlemen before my mind's eye.

The Girl's Own Paper I read for its style. Here is a sample paragraph: " 'Crumbs, girls,' cried Crackles Crompton, bursting into Dormitory Thirteen where her special chums Bubbles, Giggles and Foibles were washing their hair, preparatory to the great lacrosse match against their hated rival, St. Rawbones, the coming Saturday, 'have you heard the news?' 'Oh go and eat coke,' cried Giggles, lifting her ruddy head, thick with foam, from the basin, and cramming another fig-bar into her mouth, 'your news is always about boys, since Foibles' brother Derek took you to the Natural Science Museum last hols.' 'Oh boys are rot,' cried Crackles, a flush mounting from the top of her navy blue serge blouse toward her chestnut hair, 'boys are utter, piffling, footling rot, and you know it. There isn't a boy on earth I wouldn't give for a really spiffing hockey stick – except Daddy, of course,' she said and her liquid brown eyes grew even more liquid as she thought of Major Crompton, who was in Africa subduing native tribes. 'Miss Checkrein's stop-watch has been stolen, and until it is found the whole school is confined to the grounds.' " – This sort of writing still flourishes in spite of all the books and films about St. Trinian's; the really deep things of life are impervious to satire.

You know, I really think that I shall have to have the law on Dandiprat.

Yours determinedly,
    Sam.

*

To Mouseman, Mouseman and Forcemeat.

Dear Sirs:

Will you, as my legal advisers, give your attention to the following matter: A neighbour of mine, one Richard Dandiprat, has caused his mangy old dog Bowser to chase a skunk into my car, which I have left in my garage during my absence. The skunk has, I gather, done its worst. I know that Dandiprat did this on purpose, and now he wants to buy the car at a ridiculous price. I want to put Dandiprat in court, and take his shirt. He is a low scoundrel, and I want to show him that I am privy to his base design. If you will begin legal proceedings I shall be home in a week or so, and then we will get after him.

I hope that the rheumatism of the senior Mr. Mouseman is much improved.

Yours faithfully,
Samuel Marchbanks.

*

To Haubergeon Hydra, ESQ.

Dear Mr. Hydra:

I have now reached Wales, from which country some of my forbears emigrated to Canada. I became conscious that I was on un-English ground at Gobowen, a Welsh junctional point where the ticket-taker thanked me in the Welsh form – "ddiolch yn fawr." How pleasant, I thought, and how characteristic. And this made me wonder whether some distinctive form of thanks could not be devised and adopted in Canada. "Thank you" is excellent, but formal and English in effect. "Thanks a million" is excellent, but it has an American extravagance which is unbecoming in Canadian mouths. What would you think of "Thanks a hundred thousand"? It seems to me to strike the right Canadian note.

I direct this suggestion to you because, as Permanent Secretary to the Royal Commission on the Arts in Canada, you might be able to popularize it. If you can do so, you may take all the praise which such a happy thought will surely evoke.

Yours self-effacingly,
Samuel Marchbanks.

*

To Samuel Marchbanks, ESQ.

Esteemed Sir:

I am in receipt of your letter in which you instruct this firm, as your legal advisers, to bring action against Richard Dandiprat for having wilfully and with malice aforethought induced, instructed or compelled a skunk to commit a nuisance in your motor car.

Immediately upon receiving your communication I dispatched my efficient and discreet secretary, or confidential clerk, Miss Prudence Bunn, to Marchbanks Towers to examine the scene of the alleged misdemeanour. Miss Bunn's report was as follows:

Confidential to Mr. Mouseman: At a distance of a quarter of a mile from Marchbanks Towers the atmosphere became noticeably heavy. Asked to describe the odour in court I should use the phrase "burning old gym shoes." At 100 yards from the Towers it was clear that a skunk, or some animal indistinguishable therefrom, had committed a nuisance. In order to carry out my instructions I was compelled to soak my handkerchief in eau de Cologne and hold it over my mouth and nose. Thus protected I examined the garage, but found no evidence of violence or felony. Determined not to fail in any requirement of duty, I opened the door of the car, and at once lost consciousness, collapsing head foremost into the rear seat. I regained consciousness to find that I was being sniffed in what can only be described as a searching manner by a large white dog with pink eyes – a bull terrier, I should judge. Whether this was Mr. Dandiprat's dog Bowser I cannot say, though I have my opinion (which is not evidence). However, I can state without fear of successful contradiction, and if necessary upon oath, that a skunk or some animal indistinguishable from a skunk has been living with the utmost freedom in Mr. Marchbanks' car and has sustained an emotional shock therein.

Yours faithfully,
Prudence Bunn.

Now, Mr. Marchbanks, we cannot advise you, as your lawyers, to prefer a charge against Richard Dandiprat without further evidence to show that it was he who put the skunk in the car. My father, Mr. Jabez Mouseman, is at present unable to attend to business, as rheumatism and great age render him incapable. However, I have consulted our other partner, Mr. Cicero Forcemeat, who does all our court business and his report is as follows:

Tell Mr. Marchbanks that unless we have something to pin the skunk to Dandiprat, we wouldn't have a Chinaman's chance in court.

"Chinaman's chance," Mr. Marchbanks, is Law Latin signifying "slight likelihood of success."

Yours faithfully,
Mordecai Mouseman
(for Mouseman, Mouseman and Forcemeat).

*

To Amyas Pilgarlic, ESQ.

Dear Pil:

I am making a short stay in Wales with my Uncle Fortunatus before coming back to Canada, and to work. You have never been to Wales, I believe? A great country, and the people have immense charm. For some reason the English seem to think of the Welsh as rascals and cheats, and this unjust notion has taken hold in Canada. Of course some Welshmen are curmudgeons, but on the whole I think they are wonderfully high-spirited. As a matter of fact, the only man in medical history who died of joy was a native of the very district where I am now staying. His name was Edward Burton, and in 1558, when Queen Elizabeth came to the throne, his own patriotism and the celebrations drove him into such a frenzy of delight that it killed him. He died while roaring with laughter, and uttering loyal yells.

He was refused burial in the churchyard of St. Chad's, in Shrewsbury. Presumably the authorities took the view that no real Christian can be as joyful as that, and didn't want him making trouble among the glum ghosts. So he was buried at home. I would like to meet Burton in the hereafter, and ask whether the strange manner of his death caused him any trouble with St. Peter.

From my bedroom window I can see the hill upon which Thomas Parr lived his uncommonly long life, from 1483 to 1635 – 152 years. This remarkable old party married for the first time when he was 80, and was made to do penance for adultery when he was over 100. Rubens painted his portrait when he was 140.

I am not surprised that Parr refused to die: life here is too good to be given up – though I must leave soon.

Yours,
Sam.

*

To Samuel Marchbanks, ESQ.

Dear Mr. Marchbanks:

May I call upon you on Monday in order to borrow some books of reference of which I know you to be the possessor? I am about to begin work upon an historical study which I have long pondered, to be called *The Rise, Decline and Fall of the Toothpick, with an Appendix on the Toothpick in Canadian Lumbering.* Also, have you any old Toothpicks which I might have photographed for illustrations? My own forbears always used gold or silver toothpicks which they carried upon their watch chains. It occurs to me that someone of humbler birth, such as yourself, might have the wooden toothpicks I need.

Yours in hope,
Minerva Hawser.

*

To Mouseman, Mouseman and Forcemeat.

Dear Sirs:

Are you men or mice? Of course we must take legal action against Dandiprat. I know he put the skunk in my car because I know Dandiprat, and it is just the sort of thing he would think of. I am amazed by Mr. Cicero Forcemeat's suggestion that the case would not hold water in court. If Forcemeat wants water-tight cases, he will not get them from me. A lawyer who cannot bridge a few unavoidable gaps in evidence is a disgrace to his profession. Now, think again gentlemen!

Yours in expectation of fireworks,
S. Marchbanks.

*

FROM MY NOTEBOOKS

INTERIOR DECORATION / Had a nasty encounter with an interior decorator today. Showing me some rough cloth, he kept calling it "freezay," and it was not for a while that I realized, with stupefaction, that he was talking about good old frieze, pronounced as in the folk-saying concerning the ill-fated brass monkey. He also showed me some furniture, and said that some of it was "Louis" and the rest was "Ompeer." I quickly grasped the fact that the latter word was a fancy, frittered-French pronunciation of "Empire," but I wondered what he meant by "Louis"? The French people managed, in their dishevelled history, to have no less than eighteen kings called Louis, and he gave no clue as to which one he meant. I can be patient with many sorts of nonsense, but the nonsense of decorators unseats my reason; they want to use my money to create some sort of uninhabitable hell, filled with furniture upon which I dare not sit, and daubed with colours which scald my eyeballs. They have a way, too, of describing bits of junk as "amusing," and making electric lamps out of old chunks of trees and similar unlikely and essentially nasty materials. Better far the grotesqueries of my own taste than the fashionable foolishness of theirs.

THE CAMERA CAN LIE / Assisted this afternoon at one of those meetings where a concert committee decides what musicians it will engage for its series next season. Having decided how much money we had to spend, we passed two happy hours figuring out whom we could get for it – Monsieur Strummo, who plays the piano with his hands and feet, and who wants $5000 to do it for an hour and a half, or Signor Thumbo, who plays the musical saw all night for $25; Madame Y, who had a wonderful voice 25 years ago, or Mademoiselle Z, who is expected to have a wonderful voice in a few years? As we pondered, I looked at the pictures of the artists in the catalogue which we used; what liars photographers are! There was a picture of a soprano, looking like a virgin of 17, whom I saw recently, with a neck like the bellows of an accordion, and bags under her eyes like golf balls. There was a tenor, showing his magnificent chest and leonine head, but omitting his legs, which are about ten inches long. Another tenor was shown with his eyes closed in ecstasy; when they are opened, I happen to know that one of them is a bad glass job which he made himself, from the bottom of a beer bottle. Ah, human vanity! Ah, photographic artifice!

PERILS OF MUSEOLOGY / Visited the Royal Ontario Museum, and was concerned to notice that a lot of the stuffed animals are fading badly. The laborious researches of the Royal Society of Taxidermists, continued for over a century, has not yet discovered a way of preventing this deterioration, which can turn a beautifully striped tiger into something like a polar bear in ten or twelve years. Museums are by definition temples of probity, or the curators might touch up the animals with some of the preparations so lavishly advertised for fading hair. But if a Museum Director were to countenance such deceit he might be drummed out of the profession at the very next International Conference of Museologists. This is a dreadful ceremony, in which the offender, having been stripped naked, is locked into an Egyptian sarcophagus, upon the cover of which his former colleagues drop rare coins in an irregular rhythm, until at last he is released, raving mad, and good for nothing but light work as a Museum guard.

*

FROM MY POST BOX

To Amyas Pilgarlic, ESQ.

Dear Pil:

At last I am back in Canada. I flew home from Scotland. I made my way thither from Wales by two trains – the Flying

Scot and the Creeping Scot. What a country Scotland is, and how wonderfully the characteristics of the countryside are repeated in the people! The British Isles is rich in eccentrics, and those of Scotland are among the most flavoursome. Consider those two wonderful 18th century Lords of Session – Lord Gardenstone, who always slept with his pet pig for warmth, and Lord Monboddo, who thought that all children were born with tails! What has Canada to show to equal them?

I may tell you that as I made my way to Prestwick, I passed the Johnny Walker distillery, and the works of Shanks of Barrhead, the great makers of sanitary pottery. "The Alpha and Omega of many a good party," said my companion, raising his hat respectfully.

Yours as always,
Sam.

*

To Haubergeon Hydra, ESQ.

Dear Mr. Hydra:

I am in bed with 'flu just now and my pyjamas are a dreadful nuisance; they creep up. A lady visited me yesterday, and when I mentioned this to her she said that she had the same trouble with her nightdresses.

Then – in a flash! – inspiration came to me and I forthwith invented Marchbanks' Nightwear Stirrup. This consists of two metal stirrups, to which stout elastic cords, with clamps, are attached. The wearer puts his feet in the stirrups, clamps the cords to the bottoms of his pyjamas (or the hem of her nightdress) and the device keeps the garment in place all night long.

How does this appeal to you? As Preliminary Examiner for the Board of Patents and Copyrights, do you – as the current phrase is – go for it?

Yours in breathless anticipation,
Samuel Marchbanks.

*

To Solomon Muckbanks, ESQ.

Dear Mr. Mackbonks:

I was alarmed and displeased to receive a note saying that you are in bed with Flo, and as a servant of this Dominion I have no desire to enter into a correspondence with you so long as you occupy any irregular situation.

The device which you describe – a Nightwear Stirrup –

does not interest me, for in common with many Civil Servants of the better sort, I have employed a sleeping-bag for many years.

Yours very conditionally,
Haubergeon Hydra.

*

To Samuel Marchbanks, esq.

Honoured Sir:

The tone of your last letter was very strong – very strong indeed. As your legal advisers, we must caution you against such layman's phrases as "take the shirt off his back" and "make him eat crow," when referring to a possible legal action. We lawyers do not like such expressions: they savour of violence.

In our opinion, your case against Richard Dandiprat is uncommonly weak. You have only circumstantial evidence that he introduced a skunk into your car. Your suggestion that we should in some way bridge the gap between guesswork and certainty alarms us by its sinister implication.

Lawyers do not like to go to court. Anything may happen in court. The magistrate may be a skunk-lover, or a card-companion of Dandiprat's, or anything. Besides, courts are invariably draughty, and our court partner, Mr. Cicero Forcemeat, is trying to postpone catching his winter cold for as long as possible. We suggest that you empower us to seek a settlement with Dandiprat out of court. This is the proper legal way of doing business.

Yours for caution,
Mordecai Mouseman
(for Mouseman, Mouseman and Forcemeat).

*

To Mouseman, Mouseman and Forcemeat.

Dear Sirs:

Your mealy-mouthed letter disgusts me! Settle out of court, indeed! What are you lawyers for, if not to go to court? Eh? Answer me, Mouseman! Don't sit cringing there, in your stuffy office! Get on the job, man!

What do I care for Cicero Forcemeat's cold? If he catches cold in court I will personally send him a mustard plaster.

Now, keep your temper, Mouseman, while I explain: you say that evidence is lacking that Dandiprat put the skunk in the car. I know that he did it; I can tell by the ugly leer he gives me whenever I see him, and by the way he pretends to sniff the air when he passes my house. If you want evidence, why don't you send that sensible secretary of yours, Miss Prudence Bunn, to

Dandiprat's house, disguised as a government inspector, or a Hydro snooper, or something. Then when nobody is looking, she can nip upstairs, pinch one of Dandiprat's handkerchiefs – an initialled one – and then we can say we found it at the scene of the crime.

What you lawyers need is enterprise. I shouldn't have to do all your thinking for you.

Yours for brighter law,
   Samuel Marchbanks.

*

To Samuel Marchbanks, ESQ.

Dear Sir:

It has been brought to our attention that you have several times and in divers places alleged that our client, Richard Dandiprat, Esq., introduced a skunk into your motor vehicle and there induced, coerced or suborned the animal to misconduct itself in a characteristic manner. Should you persist in this allegation we shall take action against you for defamation.

Yours,
   Craven and Raven,
   Attorneys.

*

To Mouseman, Mouseman and Forcemeat.

Dear Mouseman:

Now look what you have done! I am sending you a letter from Craven and Raven, a firm of cheap shysters who are Dandiprat's lawyers, in which they threaten me with a libel action if I tell the truth about Dandiprat. Why don't you get on the job and put Dandiprat in court for what he has done to me? I don't want to be bothered with law: I just want Dandiprat thrown in the jug, where he belongs. Why don't you do something.

Yours passionately,
   S. Marchbanks.

*

To Samuel Marchbanks, ESQ.

Dear S.M.:

I should have written to you, I know, but I have been browsing in Canadian history, turning up the oddest things. For instance, have you read Weld's "Travels in Canada"? In his thirty-fifth letter there is this interesting passage: "It is notorious that towards one another the Indians are liberal in the extreme, and for ever ready to supply the deficiencies of their neighbours with any superfluities of their own. They have no idea of amassing wealth for themselves individually; and they wonder that persons can be found in any society so destitute of every generous sentiment, as to enrich themselves at the expense of others, and to live in ease and affluence regardless of the misery and wretchedness of members of the same community to which they themselves belong."

Obviously the Indians originated the welfare state, which we are now re-discovering for ourselves. And yet in spite of their enlightened economics the Indians seem to have felt the necessity, from time to time, of pounding, bashing, slicing and frying other Indians. A strange paradox, upon which I delight to ponder.

Adieu,
    A. Pilgarlic.

*

To Raymond Cataplasm, M.D., F.R.C.P.

Dear Dr. Cataplasm:

Ever since the death of President Kennedy American physicians have declared that rocking chairs are good for the heart, the back, and for tension of all kinds. I bring this to your attention, so that you can buy up a lot of old rocking-chairs and sell them in your dispensary at a high price. I am sure that this theory is a correct one, for all my Canadian ancestors were exceptionally long-lived and they were all great rockers. Indeed, it was reckoned that my Great-Aunt Sophonisba, during her 98 years, rocked to the moon and back again, counting each rock of her chair as 24 inches of distance covered. On a carpet with a deep pile she could go right around a good-sized room in an hour.

Do not let anyone persuade you that platform-rockers are healthy. Upon rising from a platform rocker you are likely to be kicked and severely hurt by the chair, which leaps from the ground in anger. I have seen frail and elderly people thrown down and trampled on by a platform rocker with strong springs.

I hope that you will be wildly successful with this wonderful new cardiac therapy.

Your perennial patient,
    S. Marchbanks.

*

To Mrs. Morrigan.

My dear Mrs. Morrigan:
Looking through the paper this morning I found an advertisement for a book which undertook to tell its readers how to be
"mature." "Maybe you are well-adjusted, but are you mature?"
it asked.

What do you suppose they mean by maturity? I think it is
one of the most abused words of our time. So many people say,
"He is mature," when they should say, "He is resigned to failure,"
or "His feelings are so blunted that nothing hurts him any more,"
or "He has been dead for years, but he doesn't know it."

I have never known anyone who was mature in every
respect. In men and women whom I like, even the wisest of
them, there is some strain of petulance, of caprice, of sensitive
vanity – of the things which are thought to be signs of immatur-
ity. And I would not sacrifice these endearing foibles for a chilly
perfection.

Your immature servant,
Samuel Marchbanks.
*

To Samuel Marchbanks, ESQ.

Ignoring your rudeness in your last letter, I write to inform
you that Outraged Womanhood is once more upon the march.
You have heard (as who has not?) that a quarter-pint of rum has
been added to the birthday cake of H.R.H. The Prince Edward
Antony Richard Louis. Now I ask you, what will happen when
that infant has eaten his piece of cake? Staggering, bleary-eyed,
he will drive his kiddy-car recklessly around his nursery, his
co-ordination reduced perhaps 30 per cent, until he maims his
nurse. And what sort of example is that, I ask you, for the infants
of the Empire? Rum in cake will lead to demands for rum-and-
butter toffee, and then his little bootees will be firmly set upon
the Road to Ruin.

I enclose a protest for you to sign. If you do not sign it,
never hope again to hear from
Yours,
(Mrs.) Kedijah Scissorbill.
*

To Amyas Pilgarlic, ESQ.

Dear Pil:
I don't suppose you have seen the movie of *Madame Bovary*?
I beguiled an idle hour with it last night when some fragments
appeared on TV, and was moved to reflect that there is something
deeply phoney about American actors pretending to be French-

men. And when a French classic is translated into American all illusion of French atmosphere is lost. In this piece, for instance, Mme Bovary goes to her aristocratic lover and says:

> Mme Bovary: I must have 150,000 francs.
> Aristocratic Lover: Uh don't have ut.
> Mme Bovary: Yuh don't have ut?
> Aristocratic Lover: Naw, uh don't have ut.
> Mme Bovary: (collapsing) Aw, yuh don't have ut!

Frankly this seems as un-French as if they had spoken with Scottish or Lancashire accents. There was a time when actors had a good clear speech of their own, which was not related to any special place and so was suitable for everything, but this excellent tradition was never incorporated in the movies. Ah, well –

Yours,
    Sam.

*

To Samuel Marchbanks, ESQ.

Dear Mr. Marchbanks:

May I ask you a somewhat intimate question? What do you do with your empty bottles? For some years I have been accustomed to convey mine privately to a hardware store, which used them as containers for turpentine. But now, alas, they buy their turpentine ready-bottled, and a situation of the deepest embarrassment is pending in my cellar.

My bottles are, of course, of the type generally associated with vinegar.

Yours in perplexity,
    Simon Goaste.

*

To the Rev. Simon Goaste, B.D.

Dear Rector:

I, too, have a mounting source of concern in my cellar. I know some people who drive by night to distant farms, where they dump their bottles. Yet others throw their bottles into nearby lakes. Quite a few people, the Librarian tells me, deposit their bottles in the alley behind the public library. But I, like yourself, have not as yet found any solution for the problem. Alack that the rag-bone-and-bottle *entrepreneur* has vanished from our midst!

My bottles, too, are of a sort that might well contain vinegar.

Yours unhelpfully,
    S. Marchbanks.

*

To Samuel Marchbanks, ESQ.

Dear S.M.:

Last night I was at a party at which someone commented on the premature greyness of Canadians, and at once three English people present hastened to attribute this to the great heat in our houses during the winter months.

I reflected that this theory about us and our hair has been held by the English for a century. Hearken to Susanna Moodie's opinion of our women, from *Roughing It In The Bush*:

> The Canadian women, while they retain the bloom and freshness of youth are exceedingly pretty; but these charms soon fade, owing, perhaps, to the fierce extremes of their climate, or the withering effect of the dry, metallic air of stoves, and their going too early into company and being exposed, while yet children, to the noxious influence of late hours, and the sudden change from heated rooms to the cold, bitter winter blast.

Do you think there is anything in this? Are our women so early faded because of exposure to hot stoves, or exposure to the chilling blast of Canadian masculinity? Or to both at once? This is a matter upon which I ruminate.

Yours,
A. Pilgarlic.

*

To Samuel Marchbanks, ESQ.

Honoured Sir:

You have been most indiscreet, Mr. Marchbanks, indeed you have! Now that Mr. Dandiprat's lawyers have been brought into the matter, I confess that I scarcely know which way to turn. Craven and Raven, whatever you may say to the contrary, are very astute. Indeed, they took a case to court and won it, so recently as 1924. I have consulted with the elder Mr. Mouseman, and also with Mr. Cicero Forcemeat, and we are agreed that we are pitted against some of the keenest legal talent in the country.

Oh, Mr. Marchbanks, why, oh why did you utter libel against Mr. Dandiprat? Before we know where we are this matter will come to court and, as I have told you before, anything can happen in court.

Your grieving attorney,
Mordecai Mouseman
(for Mouseman, Mouseman & Forcemeat).

*

To Amyas Pilgarlic, ESQ.

Dear Pil:

Business called me to Montreal this week, and I found myself in a nightclub. You are a wise man, and have delved deeply in the mysteries of the human mind: can you tell me why nightclubs are always so dark? In this one I could hardly see my plate, and twice dug a fork into my partner's hand, mistaking it for a devilled chop.

Returning home I found myself the sole inhabitant of the parlour car from Montreal to Westmount, where an old lady came aboard. Later in the day a few other people joined us, but by that time the old lady and I had established ourselves as the Old Families of the parlour car, the aristocracy; we frowned upon the upstarts and shushed them when they dared to raise their voices. When caste asserts itself in such trivial things, how can anyone talk seriously of social democracy? Why, the old lady and I were barely ready to grant political democracy to the poor whites who joined us at Cornwall and Smith's Falls.

Yours sincerely,
Sam.

*

To Samuel Marchbanks, ESQ.

Dear Sam:

I have been curious lately to discover what notable or merely notorious persons in history have at some time been actors. The list is surprisingly long and contains some strange fish. Did you know, for instance, that Oliver Cromwell once appeared, when a young man, in a play called *Lingua, or the Combat of The Tongue and the Five Senses for Superiority*? It sounds rather a dull piece. Cromwell played Tactus, which, as you are rather an ignorant creature, I hasten to explain means Touch. Appropriate, is it not, that a man with Cromwell's views on taxation should have played such a part? It is said that his experience as an actor inspired him with ambition to rule.

Possibly so. Many a man who has had a taste of acting takes to politics. The critics are less severe toward politicians than toward those who pursue the player's art in its more demanding form.

Yours,
A. Pilgarlic.

*

To Mrs. Morrigan.

My dear Mrs. Morrigan:

I went to Montreal this week to make a speech to a ladies' club there, and while I held forth I noticed a woman in the second row of my audience who was fast asleep. I have written the following lines to her, which I offer for your inspection, as I know you dote on poetry:

TO A LADY WHO FELL ASLEEP
DURING MY ADDRESS

> Lullaby lady,
> Lullaby dame;
> While I address ye,
> Slumber caress ye:
> Sleep without fear, madam,
> Sleep without shame.
>
> Speeches are boring;
> Tend to thy snoring:
> I, too, am bored
> But my sleep is to come.
> Restful and numbing,
> I go on humming –
> Why?
> 'Cause it brings me
> A flattering sum.
>
> Let my words weave thee
> A tent dark and deep:
> You've paid your fee, dame;
> Sleep, madam, sleep.

Yours most devotedly,
    Samuel Marchbanks.

*

To Amyas Pilgarlic, ESQ.

Dear Pil:

I suppose that even you, buried in your academic boneyard, have heard something of the uproar caused by the visit of the Royal Ballet to Canada. By a stroke of entirely undeserved good luck I obtained admission to two of their performances, and found them all that their most enthusiastic trumpeters had avouched.

One question about ballet I address to you as a scholar, and a professional unveiler of mysteries. Why do male dancers shave their armpits, but leave their chests hairy? Is the wool of the oxter in some arcane sense less aesthetically pleasing than the wool of the bosom? Perpend, Pilgarlic, and reply.

Yours impatiently,
Sam.

*

PONDERINGS

A FANCIFUL NOTION / Bruce Hutchison, whose love-affair with the Canadian nation takes many a strange turn, writes this of Sir John A. Macdonald who gave us, he says, "our first portrait of a Canadian." Here, it appears, is the portrait: "In that strange old man with the wine-red face and fantastic nose, in all the queer clutter, contradiction, comedy and tragedy of his life, we can see ourselves as in a mirror." . . . Can we, indeed? I look eagerly at my fellow-Canadians, and not a wine-red face do I behold, except in early spring, when the sun-bathing mania claims its first victims. Fantastic noses, likewise, are all too few. Clutter, contradiction, comedy and tragedy are, I confess, to be met with on every hand, but they are not exclusive to Canadians. . . . No, I cannot think that Sir John A. was much like a Canadian, or like anything else, except his excellent self. As well say that Laurier was a mirror of Canadians. If any statesman really epitomized the Canadian character and appearance, it was probably Sir Oliver Mowat. I do not hold with pretending that our exceptional and great men are made in our image. We honour and follow them for the very reason that they are not.

NOT TO THE HAVANA BORN / Read in a paper about a man in Vancouver who made one pipeful of tobacco last for an hour and 57 minutes; this same smoker said that anybody whose pipe is exhausted in less than 40 minutes smokes too fast, and lacks the proper phlegmatic attitude for a pipe-smoker. This humbled me, for although I smoke a pipe regularly I am a hasty, hot smoker, and produce vast clouds of gas and mountains of ash. A large pipe lasts me 7 mins. 30 secs. In an attempt to solve my problem I have lately taken to cigars, but they are not for me. There are two kinds of cigar smokers – patrician fellows, who look as though they had been born to smoke the finest Havana, and people like myself, who look like cannibals gnawing a finger from their latest victim. If one does not belong to the very small first class, one should smoke cigars in private; nothing makes a man look so degraded as a drool-soaked, tattered, burning stump of tobacco stuck in one corner of his mouth. Whatever a man does, he should try to do with a certain decency and regard for the feelings of others. I know that when I smoke a cigar I bring sorrow to many hearts, and regret for the degradation of mankind.

MARRIAGE IS AS YOU LIKE IT / A bachelor was talking to me about the insistent and sour propaganda against marriage which is to be found everywhere in our civilization. "Do you wonder that I am unwed," said he, "when the movies, the comic strips, the newspaper jokes and hundreds of novels and short stories are founded upon the theme that marriage is a long, rancorous fight in which a trapped and wretched male is victimized by a scheming, mercenary, domineering wife?" I admitted that this was true. Although we are assured from time to time that marriage is sacred, and that divorce, polygamy and adultery are hideous things, a surprising amount of popular entertainment is devoted to showing marriage in the worst possible light. Personally I know a great number of married people, and in my opinion most of them are much happier than they would be if they were single. Marriage is not the ideal condition for everybody, but the persistent representation of marriage as a condition of degrading servitude is nonsense. Nobody has to live in the pattern of Dagwood and Blondie or like a creation of Jimmy Hatlo, who does not choose to do so. "Cherish in your hearts some images of magnificence," said W. B. Yeats to the youth of Ireland. It should be engraved on every marriage certificate.

GOURMET'S PICNIC / There is an indescribable, pure delight about eating peanut butter sandwiches and drinking coffee in the open air. A stuffiness about both the flavour of coffee and that of peanut butter makes them a somewhat heavy combination indoors; they are oily, strong, and faintly nauseating tastes; they are things you never long for when your digestion is out of order. But to sit on the grass on a fine May day and champ mouthfuls of peanut butter sandwich, occasionally washing them down with coffee – well, I fancy there will be a good deal of that in Heaven. Fussy people object to the washing down part of this pleasure; they refer to it vulgarly as "swilling." My old school nurse, Miss Toxaemia Dogsbody, Reg. N., advised most strongly against it. But I recommend it to gourmets. And if, by any chance, you are able to add a banana to this picnic repast, you have a treat indeed. Dip the banana in your coffee for a moment; bite it; add a big mouthful of sandwich; float the whole thing in coffee – it was thus that the gods picknicked on the slopes of Olympus.

SENTIMENTAL JOURNEY / The place of my birth is not far from London (Ont.) and recently I made a pious pilgrimage thither and retraced the steps of my childhood. There it all was: the house in which I was born (for I am so incredibly old that I was born in a bed in a house, and not on a table in a hospital), the Town Hall where the Town Clerk's dog would do tricks, the church in which I sucked ghostly wisdom from the knees of several Sunday School teachers, the Tecumseh House Hotel, and – best of all – the Ferguson Opera House in which, at the age of three, I made my first appearance upon the stage as an Israelite child in an opera about Queen Esther. As theatres go, it has more of the atmosphere of the drama than many more modern playhouses, and possesses a drop-curtain upon which virtually every picturesque feature of the Continent of Europe is represented. I saw two houses which, as a child, I believed to be inhabited by witches, and The Pit – a dreadful Sheol on the edge of town, believed in my youth to be a favourite haunt of German Spies, who doubtless wanted to blow up the local canning factory. I found this Sentimental Journey quite exhausting, and returned to London in the shaky condition of a man who has had a good long look at his past.

*

COMMUNIQUÉ *(thrust under my door)*

To Big Chief Marchbanks.

How, Marchbanks:
    Maybe you not know me, Marchbanks. How, anyhow.
    You got money? I got no money. Get out of jail two day ago. Want money. Beg. Cops chase me. So I ask fat woman in house for money. You clean up yard I give you two dollar, she say. Awful mean face, Marchbanks. So I clean up dirt in nice pile behind garage. Then she say I got no cash but I give you cheque. She give me piece of blue paper. This no money, I say. Ha ha you poor ignorant savage, she say. You take cheque to bank, she say. I tear up cheque and steal three dollars worth her tools. She squawk. Cops chase me and take tools. Then I got no money and no tools. So I work one hour to dirty her yard again. Put back all her dirt and some new and stale dead cat I find under snowbank. Lots of work for nothing. Women awful hard to manage and fat ones worst. You got money? I need money.
        How again,
            Osceola Thunderbelly,
            Chief of the Crokinoles.

*

The bitter truth about women is that their minds work precisely like those of men: the bitter truth about men is that they are too vain to admit it.

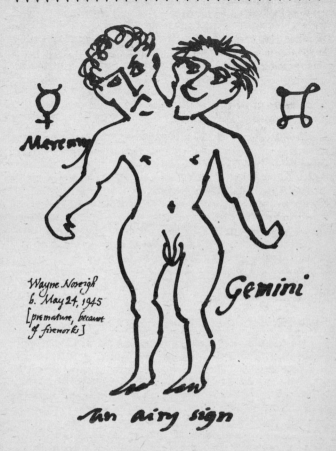

Mercury

Gemini

Wayne Noverigh
b. May 24, 1945
[premature, because
of fireworks]

An airy sign

(May 22 to June 21)

GEMINI IS the sign of the Twins, and people born under it are strongly excitable, and often experience the sensation of being beside themselves. As they are dominated by the planet Mercury, it is small wonder that they are constantly "up and down," as they themselves express it. You who are born under this sign, being of a dual nature, understandably want to have everything both ways at once, and by a little judicious application of the intelligence you have it should not be impossible to manage this; it is principally a matter of never saying anything so bluntly and irrevocably that you cannot afterward get out of it. Politics has a strong attraction for those born under Gemini and you may do well at it. It lies in your power to eat your cake and have it, too: the cake may become a little messy under these circumstances, but there is always some drawback to all good fortune.

Enchantment-of-the-Month

*✢✦✧✢✦✧✢✦✧✢✦✧✢✦✧✢✦✧✦✧✢

As you will undoubtedly want to dress in the most astrologically acceptable way, your lucky colours are yellow-brown, orange, slate-grey and gold. Wear them and you will have good fortune; if they do not become you, you will have to be content with thinking how lucky you are to have good taste. Your lucky flowers are mayblossom, myrtle, bittersweet and lily-of-the-valley, and you had better reconcile yourself to living without this particular sort of luck, for they all have a very short season and florists cannot make enough out of them to be bothered growing them in greenhouses. Your lucky stones are the beryl, the emerald and the topaz. If your fiancé wants to give you an appropriate stone, you may be excused for forgetting about the beryl and the topaz.

Health Hints for Those Born Under Gemini

You are said to be especially prone to ailments of the nervous system and rheumatic complaints. A century ago this would have been dismissed as bad luck; nowadays you may turn such disabilities into positive good fortune. To be nervous is to be one of the elect in the Twentieth Century; you can accept it either as a hobby or a career. One word of warning, however: if you intend to let nervous troubles dominate your life, you must be certain at all times to get plenty of rest, for neurosis is apt to prove exhausting to yourself and not, as it should be, to those around you. Ten hours sleep a night and a nap after lunch are the minimum for you. As for the rheumatic illnesses, they are a passport to the South every winter. They are also a protection against all the shoving, lifting and carrying expected of persons not gifted in this respect. Play your cards carefully, and a life of splendid ease lies before you.

GARDENER'S PROBLEM / I am always a little later than other people getting my garden in, but it is the autumn flowers, and asters in particular, which appeal to me. While I made my careful map of my garden on ruled paper, as the garden book said to do, I reflected how hard it is to get a satisfying bed of annuals which sounds good when you describe it. Spiderflower and feverfew look well together, but they sound as though the garden had been planted by Frankenstein's monster. And though Mourning Bride and Bouncing Bet make a nice combination, it seems to be tactless to put them together. As for bugbane, gasplant, tickseed and sneeze-weed, nothing would induce me to plant them, pretty as they are. I would not know how to mention them to people who wanted to see my garden.

YOUR PET BETRAYS YOU / A man I know who is very fond of dogs called my attention to a newspaper article today, which said that a dog grows to be like its owner. Nervous people have nervous dogs; savage people have savage dogs; stupid people have stupid dogs. Well, it may be so, though I have never seen any dog-owners among my acquaintance nosing their pets away from a garbage can, or chasing each other amorously over a newly seeded garden. But it is a fact that married people grow alike from living together, and no true dog-owner would admit that his dumb chum was less sensitive to atmosphere than his married partner. It may be that this theory about dogs throws new light on some of my friends: Professor A, the celebrated economist, has a dog which always forgets where it has buried its bones; Madame B, the fortune-teller, has a dog which cannot foresee what will happen when it goes to sleep with its tail under the rockers of Madame's chair; modest little Miss C owns a pooch of notorious wantonness and infidelity. Can it be that these beasts reveal the truth about their owners? Beware of the Dog!

THE SEX WAR / Walking home from my work this evening I passed a group of children who were busy, as children so often are, in taunting and torturing one of their number. "Teddy's got a gurr-ul! Teddy's got a gurr-ul!" they screamed, while Teddy, who appeared to be about six, denied the charge with a remarkable command of blasphemy and obscenity. I pondered upon this scene for some time. Why is it considered disgraceful for little boys to play with little girls, though a little girl who can get herself accepted in a gang of little boys gains prestige by doing so? The equality of the sexes, about which there is so much futile blather in the adult world, is unheard of among the young. Women's suffrage, and equal-pay-for-equal-work would never have come into being if children had had any say in the matter. I toyed with the idea of going back to the children and saying: "My pretty dears, the fact that Teddy has a girl shows that he is more mature than the rest of you; do you not know that girls will grow up to be the equals, in all respects, of men? Don't you know that girls will sit on the juries which will condemn you to hang, which, if I may judge by your language, is the fate to which you will all come?" But I was rather busy, and went home instead.

THE YO-YO / A child of my acquaintance was displaying her skill with the yo-yo for my benefit. She did the Elevator trick, Spank the Baby, Walk the Dog, Round the World, and the whole repertoire. I borrowed her yo-yo and attempted to recapture the skill of my younger days; as I never had any skill whatever with a yo-yo, I suppose I may say that I did so. The truth is, I was a great theorist of the yo-yo, but a poor practitioner. I could explain what made a yo-yo work, but could not persuade one to work for me. I read all the available literature on the subject; *L'Art du Yo-Yo*, by Charles Marchand, *Der Yoyokunst* and *Die Yoyoweltanschauung*, by Dr. Hermann Wurst, and *The Lives of a Bengal Yoyoist*, by Sir Roger Rattlebotham. I formed a collection of historic yo-yos and gave it to the Royal Ontario Museum which promptly put it in the basement. But I could never work a yo-yo. It demands the kind of skill shown by people who can play cat's cradle, and fold pieces of paper into lifelike birds. The mystical relationship between the yoyoist and his yo-yo, which enables him to call forth the best from the apparently inanimate object, is one of the miracles of the world of Unimportant Things.

*

FROM MY FILES

To Genghis Marchbanks, ESQ.

Dear Cousin Genghis:

I don't understand what all this fuss over Einstein's theory is about, or why so many people think it hard to understand. It seems to me that it is merely a statement in mathematical terms of what you and I and a number of thoughtful people have known all our lives – that there are a lot of funny things in the universe, and that they are all hitched up in some incomprehensible way to a central Funny Thing, and that you never really know where you are about anything. You remember Mr. Curdle in *Nicholas Nickleby*, who talked about "a completeness – a kind of universal dovetailedness with regard to place and time – a sort of general oneness, if I may be allowed to use so strong an expression"; that sums it up perfectly. Those Indian fellows who sit with their legs curled up and say they don't want to go anywhere because every place is just the same as every other place have the right idea, but they lack the insight into the matter which is possessed by such great mystics as ourselves. We are quite happy to go anywhere and do anything, because it is all the same, at bottom. All that Einstein has done is to express this in a somewhat different way.

Yours cosmically,
Sam.

＊

To Raymond Cataplasm, M.D., F.R.C.P.

Dear Dr. Cataplasm:

My memory, which as you know has never been my best feature, is rapidly growing worse. Is there some sort of degenerative disease of the brain which makes people forget things? If there is not, you can ensure yourself of a great place in medical history by discovering it. If you are going to discover it in me, I insist that it be called Marchbanks' Malady; if you use some inferior specimen you can call it Cataplasm's Spasm.

The chief symptom is a kind of seizing up of the intellect when I try to recall a name, or a bit of information; I can distinctly feel my brain contract, like a snail that has been given an electric shock; sometimes this happens in the middle of a sentence, and I forget what I was going to say, and even forget to close my mouth for some time afterward. A secondary symptom is my tendency to go upstairs for something, and bring down something else, making another trip necessary.

Do you think that anything can be done about this? I see that the insane are sometimes treated by chopping out a piece of brain: do you think it would help to open my skull and give my brain a refreshing whisk with a toothbrush?

Your perennial patient,
Samuel Marchbanks.

＊

To Mouseman, Mouseman and Forcemeat.

Dear Mouseman:

Get busy at once and apply for a patent on the greatest of my inventions – the Marchbanks Alert Mask for the Weary Face.

Thumbing through a magazine yesterday, I came upon an advertisement for a rubber mask which, pulled over the face, makes the wearer look like Boris Karloff in his role as Frankenstein's Monster. A toy, Mouseman: a trifle meant to enliven an evening party. But it touched off an explosion in my mind. Why not a rubber mask which makes the wearer look like himself — yet not himself as he usually appears, but himself at his best — alert, kindly, intelligent and yet also non-committal and reserved?

Think what a boon this would be to judges on the bench, newspaper editors, psychiatrists, university tutors, and others who have to spend hours every day listening to tales of woe, boring accounts of boring events, and threshing of old straw in general. Under the mask the wearer could relax, allowing his jaw to slacken, his lips to curl, his cheeks to slump and his dewlap to throb like a frog's, while to the observer he would seem a model of solicitous goodwill.

This will crown my career as an inventor and philanthropist. You may have stock in it to cover the amount of your bill, thus getting in on the ground floor.

> Yours triumphantly,
> Samuel Marchbanks.

*

To Amyas Pilgarlic, ESQ.

Dear Pil:

You know where I stand on dogs: I am not a person in whose life Man's Dumb Chum has played a leading role. But a day or so ago I had to attend a dog show, and as I watched the eager crowd I was visited, for perhaps the fiftieth time in my life, by the reflection that if people had to meet the rigorous standards of physical appearance which are set for dogs and other show animals it would go hardly with most of us.

The judges at the show, for instance, would have cut poor figures if the dogs had been judging them. The most important of them had a really shocking head — coarse muzzle, appledomed skull and, so far as could be seen, a poor coat. The other judge had a narrow, splayed front, a snipey muzzle, and ears set far too high. The third judge was a woman and, though I hate to say it, a poor mover, being cow-hocked and badly spaced between her shoulders, hips and stifles. None of the judges had a bright eye nor, I should say, an affectionate nature. They did not answer readily to words of command, and showed a strong tendency to turn right when it was necessary for them to turn left. Poor creatures, useless for breeding; it would have been better to drown them as puppies.

Have you observed that a miserable-looking dog is re-garded, quite rightly, as a poor-spirited creature, probably in need of worming, whereas a miserable-looking man is usually taken to be a philosopher, or at the very least, an economist? There is food for profound reflection in this.

Yours,
Sam.

*

To Raymond Cataplasm, M.D., F.R.C.P.

Dear Dr. Cataplasm:

May I ask you, as a psychologist, to explain something which I observed recently at a wedding where I was a guest. At the wedding breakfast the centre of attraction was a huge cake upon the topmost tier of which stood little effigies of a bride and groom, made (I suppose) of sugar. After the cake had been cut and slabs of it had been distributed among the guests, it came the turn of the happy pair to partake. The groom offered the bride a piece of cake on a plate, but she shook her head, smiling a secret smile. And then this girl, who for weeks had been as meek as Moses, plucked the sugar groom from the top of the cake, crunched it up in her strong white teeth, and swallowed it at a gulp.

Please, Dr. Cataplasm, what does this mean?

Your inquisitive patient,
Samuel Marchbanks.

*

To Mrs. Morrigan.

My very dear Mrs. Morrigan:

Because, for many years, there has been confusion in the popular mind regarding the terms which are used to describe periods of sleep which are enjoyed with the clothes on, I have prepared the following definitions, which I am sending to the editors of the Great Oxford Dictionary. I thought that you might like to see them, my dear friend:

1. nod: a "nod" is any brief period of informal sleep, enjoyed without benefit of bed. e.g. "I had a nod in my chair."
2. doze: a "doze" is a nod which one takes when one should not – as for instance when somebody important is talking. e.g. "I was just dozing – I heard every word you said."
3. snooze: a "snooze" is an extended nod, accompanied by sound effects, gagging on accumulations of spittle, murmuring, moaning, neighing, bad dreams, and being cross when one wakes up. e.g. "Sh! Grandpapa is having his snooze."

4. swoon: a "swoon" is an illicit snooze, enjoyed in one's office, in church or at the movies. Skilled swoonsters can do it with their eyes open (though obviously sightless). e.g. "He did not mean to snarl at the preacher; he was swooning."
5. doss: any sleep enjoyed in a reasonably upright posture, lasting for more than an hour. e.g. "He had a nice doss from lunch till tea."
6. 40 winks: the deepest kind of upright sleep, with noises, loosening the shoes, cushions, and a handkerchief over the face, e.g. "Now I don't want to hear a sound out of you children all afternoon: Daddy is going to have 40 winks."

Yours in all admiration,
    Samuel Marchbanks.

*

To Haubergeon Hydra, ESQ.

Dear Mr. Hydra:

It will hardly come as a surprise when I inform you that the pace of modern life is increasing. A statistician of international repute (myself, if you want to know) has reckoned that every adult now gets through three times as much in a day as his grandfather; we are not measuring achievement, naturally – only activity. But when it comes to running about, meeting one another, hurrying from town to town, and taking papers in and out of brief-cases, our generation is vastly superior to any of which we have record. Even the building of the Tower of Babel (which was probably on a laughably small scale) could not compare with it.

This remarkable increase in activity could not have been achieved without a great deal of hard work, and I think that we owe much to the organizers, heads of speakers' committees, pep and ginger groups, and others who have made it possible. And in order that they may meet frequently and exchange ideas on how to goad the rest of the population into even greater activity I am organizing an international association for them alone, to be called "The Friends of Thrombosis." The emblem of the association will be a small wire wheel, with a demented squirrel in it.

I am sure that there are many potential members of this association in the ranks of the Civil Service, and you, as Expediter of Needless Activities, will know best who they are. Will you get them together, therefore – I beg your pardon, I should say "alert them" – and lash them into frenzied activity in preparation for our inaugural meeting.

I intend to be Perpetual Past President of this as yet unorganized society. It is said that at the exact centre of a vortex there is utter calm. If you should want me, you'll find me at the centre of the vortex.

Yours for earlier thrombosis,
Samuel Marchbanks.

*

To Samuel Marchbanks, ESQ.

Dear Wee Sammie:

The other day, while pursuing my peaceful rounds as a junk man, I was in the house of a lady who had a good many odd bits of rock and a wheen auld jugs in a glass-fronted cupboard. "And what would ye call those, madam?" said I. "That is my collection of Chinoiserie," said she; "those pebbles are pieces of jade, and the jugs are fine old porcelain." "And why Chinoiserie?" said I. "That is the proper word for Chinese curios," said she.

As you well know, I have a cupboard of my own, in which I keep a scrap of Marchbanks tartan found in a thorn bush after the Massacre of Glencoe; our ancestor Auld Nosey Marchbanks was there as a war correspondent. And I have the sporran of our Great-great-grandfather, Close Jamie Marchbanks, which is believed to contain a bawbee, but as it is rusted shut I have never been able to get it out. And I have an empty bottle, thrown at our forbear, Fu' Charlie Marchbanks, by Robbie Burns. And as well I have a stomacher belonging to our ancestress, Sonsie Meg Marchbanks, given to her by Bonnie Prince Charlie; it is heavily encrusted with cairngorms. I am going to refer to these in future as the Marchbanks Collection of Scotchoiserie.

Your affct. uncle,
Gomeril Marchbanks.

*

FROM MY NOTEBOOKS

A LASTING CHARM / I listened recently to some gramophone records of a woman called Yma Sumac, a Peruvian who has an astonishing voice with a range of a little more than four octaves. She can tweet like a bird, sing like an ordinary woman (an ordinary woman with a very good voice, that is) and roar and rumble like the voice of Fate itself. It is a fascinating and uncanny performance. One of her songs is about the Xtabay – supposedly a poisonously alluring and beautiful woman who attracts men with her voice, once that voice has been heard, a man is her slave until he dies. I reflected that such women are uncommon in our great Dominion. Our women are not lacking in their share of good looks, but they will never attract international attention by the beauty of their voices. And yet what a potent charm a lovely woman's voice is! I would rather hear an Irish girl say something nasty to me, than hear most Canadian girls say "Take me, Mr. Marchbanks, I am yours." A man likes his eye to be refreshed, but beauty perishes. A beautiful voice, however, goes on until death, and it can call up the ghost of vanished physical beauty more readily than any other spell. Let the Canadian Female ponder this in her heart, and remedy her customary dispirited croak, caw or screech.

THOUGHTS ON LEONARDO / Had to take a bag of potatoes into the cellar of the Towers, and as I heaved and struggled with the formless monster I reflected that it is now a little over 500 years since the birth of Leonardo da Vinci who, if he had been asked to take a sack of potatoes downstairs, would undoubtedly have rigged up some ingenious machine to do so for him. Although we know him chiefly as a painter, Leonardo was one of the great engineers of all time, and never lifted anything personally, because he knew all about hoists and levers. No doubt (I reflected as my arms were dragged from their sockets and my heart was moved four inches to the left) this was why he lived to be 67 in an age when most people thought they had done well if they hung on till 40. I think it is shameful that boys are not taught a little elementary engineering at school – enough to teach them how to get a bag of potatoes into a cellar, for instance. When at last the task was done I prepared a restorative cordial and drank it, and remembered that Leonardo was a teetotaller. But then, he never lifted anything; we toiling peasants have some justification for our vices.

WILLS AND THEIR WAYS / I have been pondering about my will. As a literary document it lacks interest and surprise. Recently the wills of a number of notable Canadians have been printed in full in the metropolitan press and I have read them with interest and a degree of envy. Not that I thought much of their style; I am sure I could write a fancier will; but I was impressed by their length and complication. How can I complicate my few miserable bequests? Shall I make them conditional upon the prolonged bad conduct of my heirs? Shall I leave my library – which, at the usual second-hand dealer's price of ten cents a volume, would bring close to $20 – to a university, conditional upon their erecting a million-dollar building, with a big statue of me in the rotunda, to house it? Shall I give the Towers, with all its bills for back-taxes, to the community, to be preserved in perpetuity as a memorial to myself? Who is to get my wheel-barrow, which I coated afresh with aluminum paint last week? Shall I leave my silver tray (a splendid piece of electro-plate, nine inches in diameter in all directions) to the Ontario woman to have the greatest number of children within ten years of my demise? My present will simply won't do.

A SHOCKING DISCOVERY / At a friend's house I picked up one of those books about the Scottish clans, which explained not only which clans were which, but what families were associated with each. And, to my surprise, there was no mention of the March-banks, or even the Marjoribanks, anywhere! Can it be, then, that my family, which has always considered itself to be Scots in a mild and non-partisan way, and which has been resident in Scotland for so many years – a couple of centuries, at least – is not really Scots? Are we Marchbanks Irishmen? Or are those Marchbanks who may be found in North Wales really on their native heath? Or are we Englishmen who, for some masochistic reason, have chosen to live in Scotland? Poor indeed is that Scot who cannot scrape a connection with some clan or other, but if the Marchbanks are among these outcasts I shall bear it philoso-phically. I may even found a clan of my own, with the slogan "Hoot toot, Marchbanks!" My badge, the thistle. My tartan, any convenient motor rug.

*

FROM MY CORRESPONDENCE

To Amyas Pilgarlic, ESQ.

Dear Pil:

I am impressed by the huge new banks which have either been built, or are now in the process of building, in the fair city of Toronto. As the towers of cathedrals in the Middle Ages were thought to point the way to heaven, these vast temples of com-merce obviously stretch themselves toward the clouds as sym-bols of unimaginable wealth. And how typically Canadian these huge bank buildings are! They have a kind of stony austerity about them, and a frowning, tight-lipped expression around their doors, which strongly suggests our national attitude toward the really important things of life, such as money.

But their modern sculpture displeases me. The older bank facades were guarded by thick-waisted girls who contrived, though naked, to look unapproachable and No Fun, and by excessively muscular young men, who were tensed like young executives trying to Get Ahead. These creatures were all gods and goddesses in Banker's Mythology, and the more important ones were easily identified:

FRIGIDIUS: a god usually represented with a beard and washboard muscles on his stomach; he is the deity of branch bank managers, and is always represented with a frown, like a manager refusing to lend $50 to a small business man.

AVARICIA: the goddess of thrift, and she is usually represented naked but unamusing, with a look in her stony eyes as though she could buy a fur coat, if she wanted to be silly, like other girls.

USURIUS: the god of compound interest and he is always represented with a thoughtful look, like a banker doing a sum in his head, and wondering whether he should check it on the calculating machine.

TRANSPIRIA: the goddess of professional secrecy. She usually has one hand over her open mouth, and looks as though she were hinting to a Government Loan salesman that there is a farmer out in the county with $5,000 in cash in a coffee can under the pigsty floor, and that his wife has $800 of egg money in a Savings Account.

BAROMETRUS: the god of Future Security, and he is represented seated, gazing into the future, like a bank president trying to guess whether the credit companies will cut into his business much more during the coming year. Now and again one sees a representation of a young man chasing a young woman: this is not what you would expect, but Good Money driving out Bad.

So far as I know, this school of sculpture, done with a sandblasting machine, was peculiar to Canada. Let us cherish the examples that remain.

Yours,

Sam.

*

To Mrs. Morrigan.

My dear Mrs. Morrigan:

I was at a concert last night where a pianist played Handel's variations called *The Harmonious Blacksmith*. Of course Handel never called it anything of the kind and the name was not attached to the piece until long after Handel was dead. But the program note repeated the old story of how he received his inspiration for the piece while sheltering from a thunderstorm in a smithy. How good old George Frederick would have snorted! He loathed flapdoodle.

But this reminded me of that other legend, preserved in the old Ontario Third Reader, of how Beethoven, walking through the streets of Vienna with a friend one night, heard a piano being played in a basement; peeping through the window, he saw that a blind girl was playing to her aged father. "Alas, papa," said she, "if only I could go to the concert tomorrow night, to hear the great Beethoven play, how happy I should be! But (sob) we have no money." Without a word the great composer rushed into the cellar, sat down at the piano and played a magnificent program, improvising the *Moonlight Sonata* at the conclusion, and wowing the simple music-lover. As a child I was much touched by this story.

What disillusion awaited me when I began to look through the private papers of my Viennese ancestor, Wolfgang Amadeus Marchbanks, who was a close friend of Beethoven. Indeed, he was the very friend who accompanied Beethoven on that memorable walk. And my great-great-great uncle Wolfgang says that in reality Beethoven pushed his head through the window, and said, "Stop that row, woman; if you must play my stuff, stop vamping the bass." Beethoven was not an easy man to please.

Truth, alas, is sometimes even uglier than fiction.

Your humble servant,
Samuel Marchbanks.

❋

To Miss Nancy Frisgig.

Charming Nancy:
Last night a friend of mine showed me a book which he has, illustrative of photography during the nineteenth century. It was a wonderful book, and a revelation to me, because it contained photographs of virtually every celebrated beauty of that era. And how plain they were! Empress Eugenie, for instance, looked as though she needed a dose of liver salts, and the glamorous Lola Montez looked like the back of a hack. The Princess Alexandra was by no means what tradition avouches, and indeed the only one of the lot who really lived up to expectation was the ill-fated Empress of Mexico. Is the beauty of women, then, an illusion which cannot safely be transferred from one era to another? Would Cleopatra, if we could see her today, be merely a scruffy gypsy, and Helen of Troy a greasy girl with a garlic breath? I shrink from such conclusions, but as a philosopher I must face them.

One of the most interesting photographs in the book to me was that of Rigolboche, the dancer who made the can-can famous. Nobody thought Rigolboche beautiful, or even wholesome-looking, but she waggled a wicked shank and was full of high spirits, and Paris loved her. And when she retired wise little Rigolboche bought a high class boarding-house with her savings, and was the perfect landlady until she died at a great old age.

For years thoughts of Rigolboche have made me look at my landladies with a speculative eye. Could they, I pondered, once have been glamorous courtesans and can-can dancers? Did noblemen drink champagne from their slippers in the days before they abandoned slippers in favour of lark-heeled house shoes with scuffed toes? I have come to the conclusion that boarding-house landladies of the Rigolboche type are uncommon in Canada. Most of them are profoundly melancholy women, and if they were ever in the public eye it was certainly as hired weepers at undertaking parlours.

Yours regretfully,
Sam.

*

To Chandos Fribble, ESQ.

Dear Fribble:

I do not get to the movies as often as I could wish, but I saw one a few days ago which you really must study before you write your book on The Screen Epic. This particular Epic was presented to the audience as a wonderful evocation of the spirit of the Renaissance. It contained fine examples of three of the elements which are inseparable from celluloid epics. (1) The Virgin Heroine: in this piece she was married to an old man, and in a very pointed speech he made it clear that he had brought her up strictly as his daughter; this meant that when she was at last free to marry the hero she was, so to speak, leaping from the refrigerator into the frying-pan, which is what audiences expect. (2) The Good Villain: movie audiences like a villain to have large streaks of good in him, like the streaks of fat in a slab of restaurant ham; this gives them a comfortable feeling that although villainy is obviously fun, it is also All Right. (3) The Speech on Democracy: in film epics there must always be a moment when some minor character bawls out all the aristocrats in the cast, telling them that some day The Peepul will rise up and smite them; this is to show that all the good people in the film are democrats at heart, although they are dressed up like sixteenth century Italians; the dramatic climaxes are often complicated by the fact that the demeanour and speech of the actors makes it impossible to tell who is an aristocrat and who is Little Joe. It is doubtful if the cause of democracy is served by these tirades, but audiences like them.

At the film I sat in front of a young man who was suffering

from Teen-Ager's St. Vitus Dance, which caused him to kick the back of my seat so often and so rapidly that my head wobbled like a punching bag. Whenever the hero did anything of a spectacular nature he uttered cries like a horse in a burning stable. In spite of these annoyances I studied the piece intently. I recognized that my restless neighbour was, in the modern jargon, "empathizing."

Yours to command,

Samuel Marchbanks.

*

To Gomeril Marchbanks, esq.

Dear Uncle Gomeril:

Have you ever thought of going into the pawnbroking business? The attractions of the business are many. First of all, you have a cosy little shop, very informal in character. Then you have a wonderfully assorted type of merchandise, with a bias in favour of old watches, rusty precision tools, musical instruments of the twangling and tootling varieties, telescopes, binoculars and military decorations. It is the telescopes which ravish my soul; why anybody uses a telescope in these days of improved optical science I do not know, but obviously lots of people do. I am fascinated by telescopes, even though I have never been able to see anything through one but a lot of swimmy white stuff, like library paste in a mist. Just think of sitting in one's shop all day, peeping through the telescopes, polishing up the lodge rings, blowing the bugles, and listening to the cuckoo-clocks! And, from time to time, helping some poor needy soul with a generous loan of $2 on a bass clarinet which cost him $85 in 1917, and which you can sell for $45 any time. Oh, how delicious to be a pawnbroker, and be an Uncle to all the world.

Your affct. nephew,

Sam.

*

To Amyas Pilgarlic, esq.

Dear Pil:

The closing of the universities has caused the usual number of charming young men and women, with the chalk of the lecture-room still in their hair, to visit me and offer to revolutionize my affairs through the exercise of their talents. When I say that I have no jobs for them they look at me with pity and disbelief. They know that I am lying, that I really have excellent jobs in my gift, but that I am afraid of their brilliance. They assure me that they do not want to work for me long; they just want to learn the trade, and then pass on to better establishments than mine. The young women are sure that I have a prejudice against their sex; they are, they tell me, capable of doing anything that a man can do. I have no doubt of this, but I conceal from them the fact that too many women in an office give me a sense of living in an aviary which I find uncomfortable.

Last week I picked up a magazine which contained an article advising college graduates on – of all things – How To Choose A Boss. I should not have read it, for I knew in advance that it would give me the trembles, but I did. And it did. The perfect boss, it appears, is unlike me in every possible way. He is a jolly extrovert, with a guilty sense that he is not quite equal to his job, and with a fine understanding of the frailties of youth. He is also rather stupid, and it is easy to cozen him in the matter of pay and holidays. His temper is quick, but soon dies down. Working for this Dream Boss, it appears, is hardly work at all. It is a great big romp from morning till night.

Do I wish I were a Dream Boss? No. Depressing though it may seem, I am quite ready to go on being my curmudgeonly, reclusive, grudge-bearing, suspicious, happy self.

Nevertheless, the article depressed me. It is always depressing when one has to disappoint people's expectations.

Yours depressedly (though not to an intolerable degree),
    Sam.

*

To Raymond Cataplasm, M.D., F.R.C.P.

Dear Dr. Cataplasm:
    Whenever I am near Death, I think of you. And I have been very near Death recently, for I have had a number of conversations with an Insurance Man, and he brought me very close to Death's door on a number of occasions.

    Now I am perfectly ready to subscribe to the Scriptural admonitions that all flesh is grass, that the body is but clay, and that my soul may be required of me at any moment. But I cannot say that I like to have my nose rubbed in these indubitable truths by a man whose business it appears to be to guarantee that my survivors shall live the life of Riley after I am gone. "We've all got to face it," says he; quite so, but I prefer to face Death in the company of a few learned and picturesque old clergymen, with an unaccompanied choir singing in the distance; I do not especially like to face Death in the company of a fellow with sport shoes on his feet, a decorative tack through his necktie and a staggering number of pens and pencils in his bosom pocket. But then, I am an eccentric in such matters.

    People of my temperament, in the days of the first Queen Elizabeth, quite often kept a skull on their desks; occasionally, for added effect, the skull had a bone stuck in its jaws. This object was called a "memento mori" and its purpose was to keep its owner reminded of the fact that he too, would die. But the modern memento mori is the insurance agent, with his pencils, and whenever I see one I mutter through the General Confession, just in case.

Your perennial patient,
Samuel Marchbanks.

P.S. Do you know why women, as a rule, outlive their husbands? It is because women have too much sense to let themselves be worried to death by insurance salesmen.

*

To Mrs. Gomeril Marchbanks.

Dear Aunt Bathsheba:

Upon the whole I think you would be wrong to kill Uncle Gomeril. I recognize, of course, that mercy-killings are all the rage these days, and that any jury which knew him would probably compliment you on a good job well done, but there would be a lot of disagreeable publicity about the whole thing, and you don't know what sort of people you might have to meet before the affair blew over. Newspapermen, and such riffraff.

Don't think that I have not given a lot of thought to Uncle Gomeril's condition. He has had acidity for years, and it seems to be getting worse. In fact, I think he is the sourest old man I have ever met. It would be a mercy to put him out of his misery, though the blow to the bicarbonate of soda industry might cause a sag in the stock-market. It is dreadful to have to watch him suffer, and it is even worse to hear him, but I suggest that you look upon this as a cross, and bear it as best you can. Mercy-killing, as a means of putting inconvenient people out of the way, has its attractions, but there is always the chance that there might be some crackpot on the jury who would ask toward whom the mercy was directed.

Therefore, dear aunt, I suggest that you order in another keg of soda, buy yourself a good book on Yoga, and put this tempting scheme out of your mind. The Marchbanks are a long-lived tribe, but it will get him at last.

Your affct. nephew,
Samuel.

*

To Miss Minerva Hawser.

Dear Miss Hawser:

Your suggestion that a few people in Canada try to revive the lost art of letter-writing is a worthy one, and I am flattered that you should include me in your group. I am grateful for the copy of *The Maple Leaf Letter Writer* which you have sent me, and I have read it with great care. But there is one point on which I disagree with the book, and that is its insistence on absolutely conventional spelling. Although I am myself a fair speller, I have thought for some time that a reasonable amount of personal choice should be allowed in this matter. After all, the passion for spelling according to a dictionary is only about a hundred years old: every writer of any importance before that spelled a few words at least in his own way. If you doubt me, look at the letters of Keats, Byron, Shelley and others of that era. And during the eighteenth century and earlier spelling was a free-for-all.

Only the other day I was looking at a book of letters from the seventeenth century, in which one writer expressed himself thus: "As for Mr. A——, I esteem him no better than a Pigg." Consider that word "Pigg." The extra "g" is not strictly necessary, but what power it gives to the word! How pig-like it makes poor Mr. A——! How vivid his swinishness becomes! And look at that capital "P." It seems to enrich the sentence by calling special attention to the most important word.

I am not a spelling reformer. I am a laissez-faire liberal in matters of spelling. I do not care that our present system of spelling wastes time and paper. I firmly believe that both time and paper are of less importance than the perfect expression of the writer's meaning. Anyone who thinks otherwise is a Pedantick Booby.

Yours for orthographicall freedom,
Samuel Marchbanks.

*

To Amyas Pilgarlic, ESQ.

Dear Pil:

The Americans are a remarkable people, and I admire them quite a lot. But I never cease to be astonished at their powers of self-deception which are, like so many of their institutions, gigantic, colossal, mammoth, gargantuan, jumbo, atomic and merely large. Today I saw a book in a cigar store which was called *Ballet – The Emergence of an American Art*. Since when I wonder, did ballet become an American art? During the past years a number of American dancers have, by dint of the whole-souled energy which characterizes their nation, learned to jump as high, and twiddle as dizzily as dancers in other lands, and undoubtedly they sweat and puff more while doing so. But because ballet has gained what may properly be called a toehold in the USA, does that make it an American art? Ponder before replying.

It is always an interesting point in a nation's history when it becomes so great that it does not believe that anything has real existence outside itself. The Romans reached it. The British kept it up during most of the nineteenth century. Will Canada, I wonder, ever achieve this delightful form of insanity? Ponder well upon this.

Yours,
Sam.

*

To Chandos Fribble, ESQ.

My dear Fribble:

You know everything; can you tell me when the last writer of religious tracts died? I assume that all of them are dead, for though I am constantly receiving tracts through the mails from people who are anxious about my soul, I have yet to read one which appears to have been written within this century.

Yesterday I received a fresh batch. One of them shows a picture of a businessman (called "Mr. O. U. Foolish Man") confronted by the spectre of death in his office. He sits at a roll-top desk, on the top of which are two large bags marked "$"; he wears a white vest and at his feet is a spittoon. Now, Fribble, let us apply Sherlock Holmes' methods to this picture; the roll-top desk, the white vest and the spittoon all place it in the nineteenth century; what businessman uses such trumpery now? They all sit at steel desks and spit in the bottom drawer of the filing cabinet.

Another tract in this bunch – there were seven altogether – is called *My Experience With The Tobacco Habit*. It begins with this information: "I was a slave to tobacco for twenty years; Mother and Father used tobacco and I had the poison in my blood; Mother found me with her snuff box, when I was about eight years old." Later he says that he would pick up used quids of chewing tobacco from the street and chew them.

The last woman I know of who took snuff was my great-grandmother, who was born in 1800 and who lived to be 87; she did not chew it; she sniffed it. As for chewing tobacco, the habit has completely vanished from all settlements where civilization has a firm hold. Obviously this tract was written not less than sixty years ago.

Is no strong, new generation of tract-writers coming up to continue the work? Or will this remarkable literary form continue to rely on its past glories? Here is a meaty subject for research, Fribble.

Your admirer and crony,
S. Marchbanks.

PRECOCITY AT CARDS / Became involved in a game of Old Maid this afternoon, at the house of a friend who had preserved a wonderful set of cards, designed in the days of the Comic Valentine, and in the same convention of drawing. The characters were superb. Grocer Smallpound was there, and Harry Holdwire (who was talking on a telephone of the early, wall-instrument type). Fred Freversmoke wore a high collar and a derby hat, and was right out of the period when the smoking of cigarettes was a sign of a dashing character. Arthur Argumuch was obviously a lawyer, and Flossie Flirtsome carried me back to a day when a generalized amplitude of figure was a mark of beauty. Nora Newtogs was dressed in the height of fashion, probably by Miss Botchie Misfit, a dressmaker whose teeth, rather surprisingly, were marked "False" in large clear letters. Some children were playing, and I was astonished at their precocious gift for cards. One of them had so accurately memor-ized the creases and distinctive marks in the back of the Old Maid card that she was always able to avoid drawing it. That child will go far, but I hate to think where.

THE CURSE STRIKES / Awoke unable to move, for I had fallen victim to the Curse of the Marchbanks, which is Lumbago; it runs in our family as haemophilia runs among the Bourbons. My grandfather, who was a deeply religious man and a great student of Holy Writ, identified it as the third claw of the Beast described in Revelation. After much moaning, snorting and shrieking, and with the aid of three completely new oaths which came to me in flashes of inspiration, I rolled from my couch and huddled on my clothes. One of my legs appeared to have shortened by six inches, and my axis was eighteen degrees out of plumb, but I could walk, after a fashion, and in this pitiable state I went about my day's work. To some I was an object of sly mockery; to others my condition was a matter for a deep and unnecessary concern, for Lumbago never killed anybody, though it has sometimes driven its victims to acts of violence. It is a treacherous and feline ill, for at times it seems to abate, and then returns with renewed malignity. Asked by a friend to describe it, I racked my brains, and then said that it felt like being stabbed in the small of the back with an old-fashioned carpet-stretcher.

. . . AND CONTINUES / The trouble with Lumbago (or, to be more accurate, one of the contributory troubles) is that it rouses incredulity in people. "You've never got Lumbago!" they say, just after you have told them precisely that. Then they either laugh, which is cruel, or put on an expression that conveys their thought that you are prematurely old, which is worse. But anybody can get Lumbago, if they go about it the right way. A baby in its cradle could have it, if it was in a draught, or a bit damp, which a baby may so easily be. Lumbago, like toothache, is one of the ailments that mankind refuses to take seriously in other people. . . . My worst moment today was when I tried to carry a large parcel through a revolving door; to do this, with Lumbago, is to experience every degree of alarm, confusion, sudden pain and gross indignity.

DELUSIONS OF AMIABILITY / Attended a reunion at my old school, and met a lot of fellows I had not seen for a quarter of a century. I was astonished at the ravages which time had inflicted upon them in body, but even more by the tricks it had played with their memories. It was not a teetotal affair, and as the evening wore on dozens of them suffered acutely from Delusions of Amiability; that is to say, they remembered that I had been on much more intimate terms with them in the past than was ever really the case. I am cursed with a memory like an elephant, and I am particularly certain that I know who have been my friends and who – to put it mildly – have not; no amount of the genial juice of the grain can disturb my accuracy in such matters. Some of them obviously thought I was somebody else, some very dear old friend whom they had loved as a brother; others knew who I was, but had forgotten that I was a cantankerous and mocking wretch; some had lost all grasp of reality, and were not sure who they were themselves, but knew that they had only one true friend, and he was Marchbanks. A fascinating, revealing, uproarious evening, any way I choose to think about it.

*

COMMUNIQUÉ (*left by an Indian Runner*)

To Big Chief Marchbanks.

How, Marchbanks!

In Ottawa now, Marchbanks. Got business with government. I see by papers some Quebec Indian want government to give freedom back to Indians. No good. Indians got too much sense. Who wants to be free and work for government, anyway? Every place I look here I see sad face. Glasses. Bald spots. Government no job for happy man.

Indian here I used to know on reserve. He get ambition. Go to school. Everybody say smart Indian, give him chance. He work. And work. Now he got place in Government. Work like devil. Got black hat. Got briefcase for carry sandwiches. On reserve his name Joe Halfwit. Now he called Mr. J. Frontal Lobotomy. Sad sight, Marchbanks.

How again!

Osceola Thunderbelly,
Chief of the Crokinoles.

*

CULLED FROM THE APOPHTHEGMS
OF WIZARD MARCHBANKS

Be discreet in your loyalties, or your dwelling will not only be the home of lost causes, but the refuge of impossible people.

a cardinal, watery sign

Apollo Fishorn b. July 1, 1938 — no notice taken.

(June 22 to July 23)

CANCER IS the sign of the Crab, and you who are born under it are remarkable for your tenacity, and also for an acerbity of disposition which makes you particularly successful as critics of the arts. Your weakness is for liquids and unless you impose some discipline upon yourself you may find that you are drinking like a Pisces. In argument you who are born under this sign are extremely hard to budge, holding to a point long after others have wearied of it. Beware that this characteristic does not spread to other realms of your life, and particularly your ventures into wit, as it will serve you ill. Beware of retiring from life into your shell.

Enchantment-of-the-Month

ᐳ᠊ᐁ᠊ᐳᐁ᠊ᐳᐁ᠊ᐳᐁ᠊ᐳᐁ᠊ᐳᐁ᠊ᐳᐁ

Your planetary colours I am sorry to say, are violet, pale yellow, pale green, silver and white. Your flowers are the moonflower, and the wallflower. Your gems are moonstone, crystal, opal and any stone which is dull white or pale green. It is useless to protest; these matters were settled by astrologers hundreds of year ago, and Wizard Marchbanks accepts no responsibility for them. If these colours do not go with your complexion, blame your parents; it is axiomatic nowadays that your parents are to blame for everything that is wrong with you, anyhow. But my advice to you is that you look intently into your own soul and see whether or not the stars are right about you. Perhaps, contrary to your personal belief, you really are a palely fascinating creature. Ask your friends to give you their frank opinion. There is a bleak satisfaction to be achieved by reconciling ourselves to the inevitable.

Health Hints for Those Born Under Cancer

Astrologers agree that you are apt to suffer from gastric disorders, and that you ought to drink sparingly, if at all. Bad news, for if you are typical of those born under your sign you are interested in the pleasures of the table and inclined to be a gourmet and a connoisseur of wines. Wizard Marchbanks urges you, of all people, to pay special heed to the counsel given under your Enchantment-of-the-Month; your role, in romance as in life, is that of the passive person, the acted-upon rather than the actor, the Desired One rather than the Pursuer. If you feel inclined to rebel against this fate, give it least one good try. Slip on that filmy negligee in shades of violet and green; tuck that large moonstone into your navel in such a way that it traps the light from your boudoir candles; lie down on a white sofa and sniff a few wallflowers. Sip a glass of milk. Now, with every planetary influence auspicious, you may find that Mr. Right will steal upon you unawares, or that some hearty, protective girl with a good job may beg you to be her mate.

*

MEDITATIONS AT RANDOM

AN ALIEN WORLD / Sometimes I have the sensation of one who has survived from an earlier age into a strange and uncanny era. Rode down town today with a lady whose small child was in the back seat. Suddenly the moppet set up a great hullabaloo, and cried "Look! Look!" (In cold fact it cried "Yook! Yook!" but I have no intention of falling into baby talk.) What had excited it so much was the appearance of a horse – an ordinary draught-horse – on the street. Horses were as strange to that child as elephants. Its mother told me that the child was being taken to see – a camelopard? a unicorn? a hippogriff? – no, none of these things, but a Jersey cow which has become a celebrity, and travels around to collect money for charity. What kind of a world do I inhabit, in which horses and cows are exotic rarities, and the combustion engine, that uncanny and devilish device, is taken for granted by the smallest child? I do not greatly like animals, but I like to see them about, for I am an animal myself; the horse is my brother and the cow my sister. But by the Beard of the Prophet, the combustion engine is no relative of mine, and a world where it is supreme will not tolerate me for long.

THE ENEMY WITHIN / Agreed with a man with whom I fell into conversation that it is, upon the whole, a bad thing to keep your temper at all times. Psychologists talk a good deal nowadays about something which they call "repressed hostility," but which an old psychologist who used to do washing for my mother called "bottled-up mad." She had a great deal of mad herself, which she rarely troubled to bottle, but when she did make the effort the vile substance could be seen mounting inside her, like mercury in a thermometer. It was said of Mary, Queen of Scots, that when she drank wine it could be seen bubbling down her lovely, transparent throat, like suds in a sink; the washerwoman's mad worked the other way, rising from her bosom, up her neck, and rushing to the top of her head. Then she would unbottle some of it, at the top of her voice. But my friend and I decided that repressed hostility created tension, which led to ugly ill-nesses. It is better to beat your wife, or strike your little ones with a chair, than run such a risk. Bottled-up mad is probably at the root of many of the world's baffling diseases.

NO NO / Was talking to a man today who spent a good deal of time in Madagascar during the war. He tells me that the Mala-gasy language spoken there contains no word for "no" and none for "virginity," which may be regarded as a natural consequence. When a native of Madagascar wishes to express dissent or denial, he grins, trembles and shakes his head, which is of course a very unsatisfactory way of resisting anything. He learned this curious fact while seeking eggs to be devoured by his regiment. "Atoor-di?" he would shout at any likely-looking native, and after a time he discovered that their embarrassed contortions meant that they had no eggs to sell. Eggs, he told me, are of great importance to an army, which quickly wearies of canned food and army meat. I had not realized that soldiers were interested in eggs, but a little reflection showed me how imperceptive I had been. Without eggs, the range of possible foods is reduced by at least one-third.

THE WEAKER SEX / Read an article in a woman's magazine today called *How to Keep Your Husband From Dying of Heart Failure*. It was a sensible, well-written piece, pointing out that women are far less prone to heart injuries than men, and that women therefore should take on any heavy physical work that has to be done around a house, such as moving the furnace from one side of the cellar to another, or putting the car up on blocks for the winter. It included many anecdotes of poor, overdriven men who had been literally pushed into the Great Void by women who were afraid of such trifling tasks as carrying barrels of apples upstairs, or changing a tire on a truck. This strengthens a belief which I have long cherished, that in a few centuries women will be the larger, stronger sex, admired for their biceps and superfluous hair, and that men will be their toys and domestic comforters, exciting tenderness in the female breast by their small feet, pretty soft hands, and general helplessness. I do not think I have a heart, for I have never been able to locate my pulse, or any other symptom of a circulatory system, but I am willing to share any of the benefits of male delicacy.

*

FROM MY CORRESPONDENCE

To Amyas Pilgarlic, ESQ.

Dear Pil:

I was at a concert a few nights ago where a young woman sang *Annie Laurie* very well. I could not help wondering what impression she would have made on her hearers if she had sung the original version of the song. You know that it is always attributed to Lady Scott, who describes Annie thus:

> Her brow is like the snaw-drift,
> Her neck is like the swan;
> Her cheeks they are the fairest
> That e'er the sun shone on;
> That e'er the sun shone on,
> And dark blue is her ee . . .

And for this pleasing and rather delicate young party the singer declares himself ready to lay him doon and dee, which is an extreme measure, even for a Scotchman.

But I discovered quite recently that Lady Scott merely tidied up and watered down the poem of Annie Laurie. The original was written by William Douglas of Fingland in 1680, and he describes Annie in these words:

> She's backit like a peacock,
> She's breastit like the swan,
> She's jimp aboot the middle,
> Her waist ye weel micht span;
> Her waist ye weel micht span,
> And she hath a rolling ee . . .

This is a very different girl, and one much more to my personal taste. This earlier and more interesting Annie might be glad to know that her lover would lay him doon and dee for her if need be, but a girl with a rolling ee can usually think of better ways of passing the time.

I am all for reviving the earlier Annie.

Yours,

Sam.

*

To Haubergeon Hydra, ESQ.

Dear Mr. Hydra:

I observe with interest that the government has signified its approval of a Union of the Unemployed, which will take care of the interests of unemployed persons and do its best to assure them of a square deal. May I entreat you, as Deputy Co-ordinator of Millenial Projects, to use what influence you have to carry this a step forward, and gain approval also for a Union of the Unemployable, which I am now organizing.

It is not generally realized by capitalists and even by labour unions that there are great numbers of people who are really unsuited for work of any kind. There is nothing reprehensible in this. The same Providence which makes one man a genius makes another a stumblebum. To lay any responsibility upon the man himself is out of key with all modern thought on such matters. But it is obvious that Society – meaning those who are happily in a position to pay taxes – has a duty to the unemployable, a duty which goes far beyond the provision of workhouses. For the unemployable are by no means deficient in ability; they are all good at attending meetings, and many of them are surprisingly eloquent. If their condition were ameliorated – that is to say, if they could be assured of the fruits of labour without any necessity to perform the labour – our country would be tapping an entirely new and untried source of intellectual energy.

Under an aristocratic system of government countries supported a class which did no work and probably could not work, and that class in turn fostered the arts and sciences and brought great credit upon their native lands. A Union of the Unemployable would, in the course of time, probably do the same. The time is ripe for this daring advance in social legislation, and Canada can be first in the field. The taxpayers will howl, of course, but they are a chronically disgruntled lot, and may safely be disregarded.

Yours in hope of a favourable reply,
    Samuel Marchbanks.

*

To Chandos Fribble, ESQ.

Dear Fribble:
    It is already rather late in the year to be thinking about the summer tourist business, and such reflection immediately turns my mind toward monsters. Canada, I assert, is wretchedly under-monstered. Tourists come up here to see what? Architecture? Ha, ha! Large objects, such as cities, buildings or slum areas? They have them much bigger at home. Natural beauties? They will quickly tell you that they live in the most beautiful country in the world. No, Fribble, they come here to see strange and improbable things, and not, as is sometimes said, to enjoy the voluptuous idleness of our Canadian Way of Life.

Some parts of Canada have awakened to this fact, and have taken the proper measures. British Columbia has two splendid monsters – "Caddy" the sea-serpent, and the "Ogopogo" which is to be seen in the Okanagan Lake. Saskatchewan has a half-alligator, half-calf. In Manitoba there is a moose so large that it crosses lakes by walking along the bottom.

In this type of tourist enterprise our part of Canada is laggard. Tourists coming here are habitually underwhelmed, and if we hope to overwhelm them we must have some monsters at once. We need a genuine, eye-filling monster and it must be clearly recognizable as such, so there is no use sending me a list of names of politicians, none of whom look nearly as monstrous as they are.

If you should have any ideas, let me know.
    Your admirer and crony,
        S. Marchbanks.

*

To Miss Nancy Frisgig.

Charming Nancy:

Of course you will get parking tickets if you leave a sports-car with a mink coat in it double-parked for two hours; only soft-drink trucks are permitted such liberties. And it is hopeless to try your charms on the police; they are the kind of men Cromwell used to recruit for his Ironsides, and to them feminine charm is as piffle before the wind.

My dentist, who is a man of wide and principally sad experience, tells me that he has professionally attended soldiers, sailors, hardrock miners, tax-collectors, and other nerveless and fearless people, and that they all bear pain like heroes; the exceptions are policemen, who are as sensitive as children to a touch of the drill.

So don't try to charm them. Pay your fine, shout, "Yah, who's chicken at the dentist?", put your foot on the accelerator and get away.

> Subversively,
> Sam.

*

To Miss Minerva Hawser.

Dear Miss Hawser:

You are forever asking me questions; how would it be if you answered a question of mine, for a change? What makes my goldfish die?

A few weeks ago a false friend gave me a small bowl containing a goldfish and another black fish, with long transparent trailing stuff hanging from it, so that it looked like Salome in all her seven veils. Salome had pop eyes, in which it was possible to read the secrets of her fishy soul. Almost from the time she entered my house she pined, and it became obvious to her best friends that she was covered with a rather nasty scum. It was no surprise to me when, one day, I found her floating on the top of the bowl, a husk from which the lovely spirit had flown.

Being a humane man I trotted to the pet shop and bought a companion for the goldfish. I got a small sardine with stripes on it. I also bought a snail, as the woman in the shop said it would keep my fish from growing scummy. Within a week the goldfish was no more. The vital spark had fled. And my sardine is beginning to look a trifle peaked.

Soon I shall be left with nothing but the snail. I cannot love my snail. It grips the side of the bowl with its single foot in a way which repels me. Have you ever examined the sole of a snail's foot through a magnifying-glass? I have. It is a sight to make the gorge heave. Indeed, I almost hove my gorge right into the goldfish bowl.

What have I done wrong? Do I simply lack a green thumb with goldfish, or what?

Yours in deep puzzlement,
    Samuel Marchbanks.

P.S. Just looked in the bowl, and the snail is now in Abraham's bosom. A merciful deliverance, perhaps.

＊

To Chandos Fribble, ESQ.

Dear Fribble:

Isn't it odd how the same bit of information will crop up two or three times in the course of a week's reading? Recently I have run across several references to the nineteenth century custom of drinking champagne out of a lady's slipper, upon occasions of merrymaking. The usual thing, when the party was at its height, was to hoist the belle of the ball onto a table, laughingly remove her slipper, fill the heel of it with champagne, and quaff it off, while the lady shrieked with delight, and other fellows stood about, enviously wishing that they had thought of it first.

Plagued with a desire to test this for myself I have tried an experiment: I have a fairly new pair of bedroom slippers, and I poured some tap water into one of them and attempted to drink it. It is very hard to do this without slopping, and the liquid has a tendency to run down into the toe. It was a rather woolly drink. Further, it took my slipper eight hours to dry.

Now what do you suppose happened at those parties? When the toast had been drunk from the slipper was it then squelchily replaced on the dainty foot? And if not, how did the lady get home? So far as I know, these matters have never been satisfactorily settled. Are there any old-timers who have performed this slipper feat, who can throw light on what came later?

Yours curiously,
    S. Marchbanks.

＊

To Apollo Fishorn, ESQ.

Dear Mr. Fishorn:

You want to be a Canadian playwright, and ask me for advice as to how to set about it. Well, Fishorn, the first thing you had better acquaint yourself with is the physical conditions of the Canadian theatre. Every great drama, as you know, has been shaped by its playhouse. The Greek drama gained grandeur from its marble outdoor theatres; the Elizabethan drama was given fluidity by the extreme adaptability of the Elizabethan playhouse stage; French classical drama took its formal tone from its exquisite candle-lit theatres. You see what I mean.

Now what is the Canadian playhouse? Nine times out of ten, Fishorn, it is a school hall, smelling of chalk and kids, and decorated in the Early Concrete style. The stage is a small raised room at one end. And I mean room. If you step into the wings suddenly you will fracture your nose against the wall. There is no place for storing scenery, no place for the actors to dress, and the lighting is designed to warm the stage but not to illuminate it.

Write your plays, then, for such a stage. Do not demand any processions of elephants, or dances by the maidens of the Caliph's harem. Keep away from sunsets and storms at sea. Place as many scenes as you can in cellars and kindred spots. And don't have more than three characters on the stage at one time, or the weakest of them is sure to be nudged into the audience.

Farewell, and good luck to you,
S. Marchbanks.

*

To Haubergeon Hydra, ESQ.

Dear Mr. Hydra:

The five-day week is undoubtedly a fine thing; the less work people do the less mischief they are likely to cause. It has been my observation that it is men's work, rather than their recreations, which create trouble. But, Oh, Mr. Hydra, do you think you could do anything to prevent those who work a five-day week from using Saturday to pester those who don't?

I make this appeal to you, as Special Commissioner of Nuisances. There is springing up in our fair land a whole class of people who use Saturday morning, especially, as a time for social calls, practical jokes, foolish questions, and kindred knavery. As one who works a six-and-a-half-day week I find that it adds intolerably to my burdens. Could you not form a Sixth Day Alliance, to protect Saturday workers from the floating population?

Yours distractedly,
Samuel Marchbanks.

*

To Samuel Marchbanks, ESQ.

Dear Mr. Marchbanks:

Capital news, Mr. Marchbanks, sir! At last we see our way clear to bring your case against Richard Dandiprat to court. I fear that perhaps the proceedings may not be precisely as you have envisioned them in your layman's imagination. You have asserted that Mr. Dandiprat, with malice aforethought, induced a skunk to enter your car, and there to comport itself in such a manner as to constitute a nuisance. But as you appear to have lost all the documents which establish you as owner of the car our case breaks down at that point. We can only bring action against Dandiprat on charges of having behaved with cruelty toward a skunk, by incarcerating it in a stationary vehicle without food or water. You enter the case only as undoubted owner of the garage in which the car stood at the time. If the defence should claim that you were negligent in not locking the garage you may be censured by the judge, but I doubt if you will be asked to share Dandiprat's fine.

If we are very fortunate we may be able to get this case on the docket for the Autumn Assizes; otherwise it will hold over until Spring. The law is a dreadful engine, Mr. Marchbanks, and when set in motion it moves with frightening speed.

Yours in high glee,
Mordecai Mouseman
(for Mouseman, Mouseman and Forcemeat).

*

To Amyas Pilgarlic, ESQ.

Dear Pil:

This is a world of rush and bustle, but I have found one point of calm in the maelstrom, one unfailing fountain of surcease. For some years I have subscribed to two or three English weekend papers, deceiving myself that I do so in order to keep up with what is doing abroad. I take the *New Statesman*, and the *Spectator*, and the *Sunday Times*, but I have long realized, at the back of my mind, that I do not read these to keep up with the news, but to put a brake on the news. When I get these journals – or I suppose they should be called hebdomadals – they are about a month old, and I have the delightful sensation of reading about the past, laughing at the predictions which have been proved untrue, and the fears which have become groundless. It is a thoroughly god-like amusement.

Why they arrive so late I cannot really discover. In my grandfather's day it took about a month to get a paper from England, and it still does. The English attitude toward such things is leisurely. I imagine the Editor of the *New Statesman* saying to his secretary, "Oh, Elsie, have you sent the parcel to that Canadian chap – Matchbox or whatever his name is?" And Elsie says, "Not this week; the new ball of twine hasn't come yet; I shall attend to it first thing next week." Then the Editor says, "Oh, plenty of time; the mail-packets leave Tilbury every second

Thursday." And thus it goes. I pray that modern efficiency may never reach the circulation departments of the radical journals, or I may lose this delicious sensation of repose.

Your crony,
Sam.

*

A GARLAND OF MUSINGS

BARN ENCHANTMENT / Visited a friend who has recently acquired a house with a barn behind it. I am fond of barns; there is a pleasant air of mystery about them, particularly when they have not had cement floors, aluminum mangers and fluorescent lighting installed in them. This was a good old barn, smelling still of horses, and it carried me back to my childhood so powerfully that I climbed the ladder into the haymow, and discovered that I am either less nimble than I was as a child, or that the ladders leading to haymows are frailer. The ladder trembled, and I trembled, but at last I reached the top and cracked my head smartly on a beam which was over the ladder-hole. The loft was just as dark and full of exciting possibilities as I had hoped it would be, and when I dimly descried the stuffed head of a bison hanging on one wall my cup of joy was full. A visit to a good barn is like a plunge into the fountain of youth.

DISINGENUOUS DEDICATIONS / Picked up a book, a new edition of a classic of fully a hundred years standing, and found that it had been dedicated, not by the author, but by the illustrator, to somebody called Alison. There were the words, "The illustrations in this volume are dedicated to Alison." I consider this impertinent. If one may dedicate the illustrations of a book, why not the binding? Why should not the paper manufacturers insert a note saying, "The genuine mashed pine parchment upon which this volume is printed is dedicated to Susan"? . . . The whole business of dedications is interesting. What does a dedication really mean? I have never heard of an author who made over the royalties on a book to the person to whom it was dedicated. The person to whom the dedication is addressed – the dedicatee, I suppose he should be called – has no control over what appears in the book. I shrewdly suspect that dedications are, in nine cases out of ten, attempts on the part of an author to seem generous without incurring any painful outlay of money. The saddest dedications are those which scholars make to their wives, as when the dedication of *A New Exegetical Consideration of Second Thessalonians reads*, "To Effie, who read the proofs and prepared the index."

CAPTIVE AUDIENCE / Received a letter from a wretch who is obviously suffering from a bad case of Stenographer Fever. This disease, which is well known in business circles but unaccountably ignored by medical science, is a condition in which a man dictates letters to impress his stenographer, rather than the true recipient of his message. His letter becomes rhetorical and hectoring in tone. He tends to call his correspondent by name several times, thus; – "Now, Mr. Marchbanks, as you are no doubt well aware, it is not my custom to mince words with such a man as you, Mr. Marchbanks, seem to be . . ." – generally I deal with such letters by replying in this strain: – "Samuel Marchbanks has received your note. His answer is No." . . . No man, we are told, is a hero to his valet, but the world of business abounds with men who wish to be heroes to their stenographers and to this end they soar and bombinate, keeping an appreciative eye on the Captive Audience on the other side of the desk.

*

FROM MY FILES

To Raymond Cataplasm, M.D., F.R.C.P.

Dear Dr. Cataplasm:

I have just had a brilliant idea which, if you can make it practical, will revolutionize medical science. I am, as you know, of partly Celtic ancestry, and I have for many years been fascinated by the institution of the Sin Eater, once so popular in Wales and its border country. At every funeral there attended some old man who, at the proper time, accepted across the body of the corpse a piece of cake, a cup of wine, and a small piece of money; he ate these – not the money, of course – saying before everyone present that he took upon him the sins of the dead person, whose soul was then free to go to Heaven without any burden upon it.

Could not medical skill arrange for someone, to be called the Fat Eater, to undertake a similar service for people whose metabolism disposes them to put on excess weight? As the stout party sat down to meals he could hand a few victuals across the table to the Fat Eater, on the understanding that the latter would take upon himself any poundage which might result from his feeding. And thus, while the employer had the fun of the food, the Fat Eater would take on the burden of the weight.

Like all great ideas, this is essentially simple. It just needs a little working out, which I am sure you can manage easily.

Your perennial patient,
Samuel Marchbanks,

To Amyas Pilgarlic, ESQ.

Dear Pil:

I attended an admirable concert recently and enjoyed myself very much, but whenever the singer was about to tackle a song in a foreign language I would cast my eyes at the translation of the words which was included on my program, and would see something like this: "Beautiful lips, shuffling to and fro with indecision, why don't you render me the delicious happiness to say yes, again yes, oh yes, lips, hurry up lips, yes, yes." I am no great hand at understanding German and Italian, but I venture to say that the words of the songs were on a slightly higher literary level than the translations indicated.

Do you suppose that in Italy and Germany songs in English are translated in the same way for concert audiences? If so, I can imagine *Drink To Me Only With Thine Eyes* working out something like this: "Let us agree, when drinking, to employ the eyeballs only; similarly with kisses; I sent you some flowers recently and you sent them back after blowing on them; they are still alive but are impregnated with your personal odour."

Could UNESCO do anything about this confusing question of translating songs?

Your crony,
Sam.

*

To Haubergeon Hydra, ESQ.

Dear Mr. Hydra:

There is a matter of some delicacy which I feel should be brought to your notice, as Deputy Expediter of the Plan for the Beautification of the Dominion Capital. I had occasion to visit Ottawa recently, and as I entered the city by train, and again as I left it, I was painfully struck by its resemblance to a foreign capital which I shall only describe as M-sc-w.

Pause, Mr. Hydra, before you put the RCMP to work to investigate me. I mean no disloyalty. Quite otherwise. This resemblance grieved me more than I can say, and I would like it to be minimized. I am sure that it has not come to your personal attention because, like all Civil Servants, you rarely leave the capital, and when you do you take a sack full of papers to work at on the train, and never look out of the window. Consequently you have never been struck, as I was, by the resemblance of Parliament Hill to the Kr-ml-n. Those spires, surrounded by grey mist, that air of brooding secrecy, that sense of doom — oh, Hydra, they won't do at all! They give quite the wrong impression.

Do you think that in beautifying the capital you could alter all its architecture to something jollier – something more suggestive of democracy at work? Could the spires be swelled out a little, so that they became domes? Or perhaps the spires could be sawed off at the roots? For I assure you, sir, that those spires, rising above the low skyline of Hull, give quite the wrong impression to the visitor.

Yours for democratic architecture,
S. Marchbanks.

*

To Samuel Marchbanks, ESQ.

Dear Marchbanks:

This lawsuit you are bringing against me is getting to be a nuisance. I only put the skunk in your car for a joke. Have you no sense of humour?

I'll tell you what I'll do. You like pictures, I believe. If you will tell your lawyers to drop the case I'll give you a picture my Aunt Bessie brought back from her tour of Italy before Great War I. I think she said it was Venus Rising from the Sea, by Botticelli. The family have always called it The Stark Tart, and we keep it in the attic. I believe it is the original, but maybe it is just a copy. Anyhow, it looks like the kind of thing you would like. It is a little stained by damp, but otherwise all right.

If this isn't generosity, I don't know what you could call it.

Yours fraternally,
Dick Dandiprat.

*

To Richard Dandiprat, ESQ.

Presumptuous Dandiprat:

I would call it gross impudence, and an attempt to clog the mighty engine of justice. Keep your foreign pornography, wretch, to comfort you in prison.

Disdainfully,
Marchbanks.

*

To Chandos Fribble, ESQ.

Dear Fribble:

You are a great investigator of the phenomena of our civilization. Can you tell me why magazines are getting smaller? Yesterday I wanted a magazine – an unusual thing with me – and hied me to a news stand. I counted 82 magazines on the racks, of which 53 were little ones. Many of these were called Digests of one sort and another. I have noticed the tendency for years for big papers to shrink into magazines, and for magazines to dwindle into digests, but I did not realize that it had gone so far.

Where will it all end? After digestion – what? The smallest of the digests – a new one – was about the size of a pocket notebook. What will happen if somebody decides to digest it? The result will have to be read with a microscope. Not that I care. They can get as small as they like without any protest from me. But I am curious to know the reason for this sudden passion for miniature magazines. Is it shrinking reading matter to suit the shrinking brain?

Yours nosily,
Samuel Marchbanks.

*

To Amyas Pilgarlic, ESQ.

Dear Pil:

Last week I was bidden to a graduation banquet where a large number of students – after consuming the tomato soup, green peas and deliquescent ice cream which are obligatory at such orgies – listened to speeches of good advice from their elders, and made a few speeches themselves.

What particularly impressed me was that the elders who spoke all assured the young people that they were going out into a World of Chaos, and the young people all agreed with them.

This moved me to ponder that I was born into a world of chaos – the chaos of the moment being the First World War. My childhood was passed amidst the chaos of the Post War World, and then came the chaos of the Depression; this, in time, gave way to the chaos of the Second World War, and now I wallow in the chaos of the Atomic Age. This is a pretty good record for one life – chaos every minute.

In spite of all this chaos, however, most people seem to lead humdrum lives, and badly want livening up. Do you think we should organize a Chaos-of-the-Month Club, guaranteeing to supply all members with something really unnerving every thirty days? For I greatly fear that most of those students, rushing eagerly out into a world of chaos, are going to find that their particular part of it quickly becomes a deadly routine.

Yours for more varied chaos,
Sam.

*

To Waghorn Wittol, ESQ.

Esteemed Wittol:

You write to ask me if I think that the smoking of a pipe would help you to bear your troubles more easily. You refer, I gather, to the unaccountable absences and occasional eccentricities of Mrs. Wittol. You mention the fact that Dr. Albert Einstein, in accepting a life membership in the Montreal Pipe Smokers Club said: "Pipe smoking contributes to a somewhat calm and objective judgement in all human affairs." Far be it from me to contradict such a man, but I feel that I should warn you that pipe smoking brings its own troubles.

Of course, if you buy one pipe and smoke it until it threatens to asphyxiate you, using any kind of tobacco you can get cheap, you may have no difficulty. But if you aspire to be a gentleman pipe-smoker you are in for a rough time. You will be overwhelmed with advice from pipe-smoking friends about kinds of tobacco, how to stuff your pipe, how and when to clean it, and how to knock the ashes out of it. You will learn to be anxious about the "cake" inside the bowl, which must be kept precisely one-sixteenth of an inch thick – no more and no less. You will worry about making each pipeful burn evenly, and you will agonize if your bowl grows hot. You will find that you cannot talk when smoking, and that you cannot think about anything except your pipe. You will lust after pipes which are beyond your means, and you will despise people who smoke cheap pipes and ordinary tobacco. You will, in short, be about as calm and objective as a whirling dervish.

I smoke a pipe myself – a dirty little affair made, I think, of pitch-pine. I tried to be a gentleman smoker but it was beyond me. Why don't you take snuff, which is much easier and will make your eyes water so much that you won't notice what Mrs. Wittol is up to.

Yours without prejudice,
S. Marchbanks.

*

To Chandos Fribble, ESQ.

My good Fribble:

You are a man of enquiring mind, and a psychologist of note. Can you explain the lamentable decline in the art of face-making among modern Canadian children? You will recall that when we were boys the making of faces was taken seriously; children devoted hours to the evolution of new and horrifying faces, and a certain distinction attached to the boy or girl who led his circle in this respect.

The child of today seems utterly dead to the delights of

masterly mugging. Now and again they stick out their tongues in a lackadaisical fashion, but not far. I remember the days when tongues were tongues, and nothing under four inches of exposure was considered respectable. Gifted children could turn the tongue upward, touching the tip of the nose, and exposing the fraenulum, or blue string, which is one of the tongue's special features. Dragging down the under lids of the eyes was carefully cultivated, so as to expose the maximum of wet red flesh beneath the eyeball. The nostrils were drawn upward with the fingers. The ears were violently wiggled. The combinations of these basic distortions were many and, in capable hands, produced brilliant effects. But all of this glory is departed. Why is it so, Fribble? Has some of the elasticity gone from youth?

Yours reflectively,
S. Marchbanks.

*

To Mrs. Kedijah Scissorbill.

Dear Mrs. Scissorbill:

It is useless to reproach me because I have publicly confessed that I am a regular reader of the comic strips. I have read them ever since I could read anything, and I am not likely to change now. Your concern about comics arises, I think, from the fact that you do not understand them. They are not as great an influence on the lives of their readers as you think. For instance, I read every day certain adventure strips, not because I like the characters but because I detest them. I sneer cruelly at their dreadful predicaments, their dangerous, overstrained lives, and at the tawdry charms of their women. I hope, in an idle sort of way, that they will at last get themselves into a fix so desperate that they will never escape. It troubles me not at all that they never do so.

There are certain strips, on the other hand, which are social comment. By reading them I can find out what millons of my fellow creatures believe and what they think.

And finally there are a few strips of great strength, of imagination, or of whimsical charm. I read them quite simply because I like them.

You may say that I might devote the ten minutes a day I give to the twenty comics I read to some better purpose. I reply that I doubt it. Hoping that the strain of policing your fellow citizens is not proving too much for you, I am

Yours unregenerately,
Samuel Marchbanks.

To Samuel Marchbanks, ESQ.

Esteemed Sir:

The costs of pursuing your case against Richard Dandiprat, Esq., are mounting. As you know, there are many charges involved in legal proceedings apart from the charge brought in court. (Ha, ha: a legal jest, Mr. Marchbanks, and a great favourite with Mr. Mouseman, senior; pardon me for bringing it up but I could not help myself.) There is the cost, for instance, of having all the relevant documents copied in octuplicate. You may say that there were no relevant documents in your case, but you would be wrong; we have created several. That is part of the service a lawyer offers his client. And there are carrying charges, as well; these are the fees required to induce your lawyer to carry your case in his head; these are utterly indispensable. And there are incidental charges; for instance during the typing of some documents related to your case a typewriter ribbon frayed away to a juiceless shoe-string; there was nothing to be done but to replace it, the first time this has been necessary since the purchase of the machine in 1907.

We never plague our clients for money, but we suggest to you that we do not live upon air, though we have been known to live upon heirs. (I crave forgiveness, sir; another pleasantry of the elder Mr. Mouseman; it slipped out, somehow.) A little something to be going on with would be a lovely midsummer surprise for

Yours faithfully,
Mordecai Mouseman
(for Mouseman, Mouseman and Forcemeat).

*

FROM MY NOTEBOOKS

OIL ODDITY / Had the pleasure today of viewing a beautiful indoor garden, owned by some very wealthy people, and marvelled foolishly because there were no weeds in it. Indeed, the earth had been topped with some black, velvety substance to set off the flowers which grew there. But what really made my eyes pop was a collection of ferns and decorative plants, the leaves of which had been lightly oiled in order to make them shine! This is gardening on a level undreamed of at Marchbanks Towers, where the only thing I ever oil is the head gardener (myself) when half an hour's unbroken work has sapped his vitality. I apply a special oil inwardly. However, I am thinking of trying this treatment on my aspidistra, using what remains in a bottle of oil left at the Towers by a constipated visitor.

LAST ENCHANTMENTS OF THE MIDDLE AGE / To the movies, to see *Ivanhoe*, and enjoyed it thoroughly. It departs a good deal from the novel, but I am not one to complain of that, for Scott always put enough plot in a single book to last Hollywood for a year. Athelstane of Conningsburgh was cut out entirely, but I did not miss him; King Richard was trimmed to a mere sliver, but what remained was satisfactorily Lion-Hearted. The only change I deplored was in the death of Brian de Bois Guilbert; in the film he and Ivanhoe fought to the death with a Boppeur de la Tete (a chain with a spiky ball on the end) and a Hacqueur du Corps (a fire axe); my studies in mediaeval armoury enabled me to recognize these at once. But in the book Brian died in the most dramatic way possible; he simply exploded, a victim of the contending passions of love and hate, and died one of the most interesting psychological deaths in all literature. George Sanders is an excellent actor, with a vast repertory of sneers and leers, and he could have given us the biggest death-scene since Jumbo was hit by a train at St. Thomas. But Hollywood still fears these subtleties, and the final battle reminded me of one of my enraged assaults upon the furnace at the Towers.

IGNORAMUS / To my dentist, and as I sit in his chair I look through a large window toward the spire of a church which is surmounted by a cross. This reminded me of the inscription on Strindberg's tomb – *Ave Crux Spes. Unica.* I know what this means, but it is hard to put it into English. "Hail Cross, You Unique Thing" does not sound right and "Hail the Cross, It's The Only Thing" sounds like an advertisement for a patent medicine. But puzzling over this matter slightly distracted my mind while the dentist moved a small machine shop into my mouth and arranged things to suit his taste. Why such an old snorter as Strindberg chose such a pious inscription I cannot guess. . . .

Realized later, when the pain was going out of my jaw, that of course it meant "Hail, Cross, our sole Hope." It is translation of this quality that made me the despair of many a Latin teacher. I am an impetuous, rather than a pedantic, translator.

*

COMMUNIQUÉ (*wrapped 'round a stone and thrown through my window*)

To Big Chief Marchbanks.

How, Marchbanks:

I lucky Indian, Marchbanks. Why? I tell. Last week Chief Fishbone-in-Throat die. Young man, Marchbanks. Only 102. Once I nearly marry his daughter, Princess Blocked Drain. Now Fishbone dead, Ottawa want succession duties. They take wigwam, take wampum, take truss off corpse. Bury Fishbone all busted. Now Blocked Drain poor woman. Owe Ottawa money. She offer Ottawa corpse of Fishbone but Ottawa refused because of rupture. Only want fancy corpse. I lucky Indian, Marchbanks. If I married Blocked Drain might have to work too, now. Instead I got job on roads. Wave red flag. Authority, Marchbanks.

How, again!

Osceola Thunderbelly,
Chief of the Crokinoles.

*

CULLED FROM THE APOPHTHEGMS
OF WIZARD MARCHBANKS

Wisdom is a variable possession. Every man is wise when pursued by a mad dog; fewer when pursued by a mad woman; only the wisest survive when attacked by a mad notion.

Mrs. Morrigan
b. Aug 1., 1900

very grey

Sun

Leo

(July 24 to August 23)

LEO IS the sign of the Lion. You who are born uuder it are born to rule, and to have your own way in everything, and therefore you should take special care never to be associated with persons born under Aries or Taurus, for they will dispute with you for top place. Avoid persons born under Gemini, for they may overthrow you by their subtlety. Have nothing to do with those born under Cancer, for their criticism may undermine you. The Leo-born have a tendency to show off; this should not be resisted for, contrary to opinions spread chiefly by those born under Cancer, it is impressive and strengthens the feeling that you should be allowed to do as you please. This is what is important; get your own way, and if any misfortunes result therefrom, you will probably not notice them, or will attribute them to some other cause.

Enchantment-of-the-Month

꙳⚙꙳꙳⚙꙳꙳⚙꙳꙳⚙꙳꙳⚙꙳꙳⚙

Lucky indeed are those born under Leo. Look at your fortunate colours – blood-red, orange, scarlet and yellow! Whee! And your lucky flowers – marigold and peony! And your lucky stones – diamond and ruby! If this doesn't make you happy with your lot you are hard to please indeed. You will observe that red is lucky for you wherever it appears, but be sure you keep it for yourself. A Leo-born husband will be likely to think that his wife always looks best in a red dress; his Ideal Woman is dressed in red from top to toe, has red hair and a flaming makeup, and is sitting in a red chair eating red jelly. Try to moderate this passion. Do not force red meat upon your Cancer-born friends, when they are yearning for a bowl of blanc-mange. Get it through your head that red is for *you* to wear, and that it is not necessary for you to see red all the time.

Health Hints for Those Born Under Leo

You have wonderful health, but you must be careful of your heart and back. This will not be easy, for you are the kind of fellow who tries to move the piano single-handed, and delights in being anchor-man when tug o' war is played. If something goes wrong with your heart, don't tell people about it. Remember, your character is founded upon that of the Lion, and a hang-dog Lion is not a pretty sight. A Lion nobly inactive, however, is just as impressive as a Lion on the rampage. If you have perfect health, which is highly probable, don't tell people less fortunate that they could be like you if only they would try. It is not true and they might give you a saucy and disconcerting answer.

*

MEDITATIONS AT RANDOM

BIBLE CONUNDRUM / A small child begged me to tell her about Adam and Eve, which I did. I then scored a great success by asking her a Bible riddle which was a favourite of my childhood: "What eight men in the Bible milked a bear?" The answer, to be found in Genesis 22:23, is Huz, Buz, Kemuel, Chesed, Hazo, Pildash, Jidlaph and Bethuel, the eight sons of Abraham's brother Nahor, by his wife Milcah; the Hebrew reads – "these eight did Milcah bear to Nahor, Abraham's brother." I am full of hallowed jocosity of this sort.

INFORMATION SCORNED / To the movies and sat first of all behind a small boy whose hair had obviously been cut at home; the poor child looked as though an Indian had begun to scalp him, but had been called out on strike when half done. Behind me sat a woman with a package of sticky popcorn; I did not much mind her noisy champings, but it bothered me that she dropped a lot of the goodies on the floor, and they rolled down under my feet and gave me a sense of treading on broken eggs. So I moved, and found myself behind two girls, both at the very pinnacle of romantic yearning. The film, however, seemed to be beyond their modest intellectual grasp; it was about a period of history before the advent of the combustion engine, and everybody went everywhere on horses or behind horses. At one point a lady entered a room and said that she must stay a while because a shoe had been lost. The girls whispered busily between them, and then agreed that she must be crazy, as she was wearing both her shoes, as any fool could plainly see. I leaned forward help-fully, "Her horse lost a shoe, poppets," I said. They viewed me with the scorn of youth. "Drop dead, Gramp," said one of them; "since when did horses wear shoes?" Since when, indeed?

UNEARNED INCOME / Have been looking over the questions the census-taker will ask me. One of them is an enquiry as to how much money I earned last year. The answer to this will be, "about $125." Of course I had more money than this, but I didn't earn it. The Government itself says that I didn't. For I get my living as a writer, and the Government makes it very clear in its Income Tax forms that what a writer gets is Investment Income, comparable to the guilty gold which the Idle Rich derive from their holdings in Stocks and Shares. The census-taker will stare about him in amazement, his eye straying from the rich tapes-tries upon my walls to the priceless products of old Persian looms beneath his feet; as I scratch a match upon a rare piece of cloisonné, and scissor a chunk out of an early Picasso in order to mend a hole in my shoe, he will scratch his head and wonder how I came by such Byzantine luxury without earning it. But if my Government says that I do not earn my money, I am not the kind of saucy fellow who will suggest that they do my job, and see if it feels like work. No, no! I am behind my Government one hundred per cent, and when it says my labour is idleness, I knock my head upon the floor and cry Selah!

REVIVING A LOST ART / Had occasion to look at a display of wall-paper. Fastening decorative paper to walls is an old trick, which came into favour when it became too expensive to use decorative cloth. The decorative cloth fastened tight to the wall followed the painted cloths which the people of Tudor days hung loose upon their walls, and these in their turn were substitutes for tapestries. Personally I think it might be interesting to return to tapestries, for in these days of labour-saving household devices women have plenty of leisure time for tapestry work. Modern tapestries, of course, would have to have modern themes. A really loving wife might work for ten or twelve years to create a tapestry showing how her husband had worked up from the lowly post of office boy to be vice-president in charge of the mail-order department, along the lines of the Bayeux Tapestry. As a substitute for wallpaper this might take rather a long time to prepare, but it would have a personal touch and, after the husband had been fired or demoted, a pleasingly nostalgic quality.

*

FROM MY ARCHIVES

To the Rev. Simon Goaste, B.D.

Dear Pastor:

Don't you think it is high time that the Americans had their own translation of the Bible? Recently I saw Cecil B. DeMille's film of *Samson and Delilah*, and afterward I re-read the story as it is written in Judges 13-16; it was clear to me what DeMille had gone through, trying to turn Samson and Delilah into good, respectable Americans.

Consider: in the Bible version Samson carelessly allowed twenty years to pass between his strangling of the lion and his adventure with Delilah. Such a lapse of time would have made him at least forty when the film ended – practically an old man by Hollywood reckoning. In a new translation this period of time could be tactfully left out. And it is recorded also that Samson had an adventure with a lady about whose virtue the Scriptures, in their coarse way, leave no doubt. In fact, it appears that Samson was not A Nice Clean American Boy but a rowdy old delinquent. This blot on his character could be glossed over in a new translation, as it was in the movie. And there is also the flat statement that Samson set fire to the tails of a lot of foxes; the SPCA would certainly not have tolerated that if it had been shown in the film.

What the USA needs is a translation of the Bible all its own. It is now the dominant Western power, and should avail itself of the traditional privilege of a dominant power to impose its religion, or its version of an existing religion, upon the rest of the world. There is much in the Bible that is undemocratic and un-American. Indeed, I put it to you that the implication that the Supreme Being was not democratically elected to that position casts grave doubts upon the moral magnitude and spiritual significance of the Constitution. It is time to abandon the King James Version, with its seventeenth century cast of thought and its strongly English slant, and to adopt something more in keeping with the Gospel according to Washington.

> Your expectant parishioner,
> Samuel Marchbanks.

*

To Samuel Marchbanks, ESQ.

Dear Mr. Marchbanks:

One of the things that is wrong with the world today, but which nobody ever complains about, is that children are not as religious as they used to be. No doubt about it, a religious child is a good example to its elders, and children have a duty in this respect which they are neglecting.

Two fine examples of youthful piety have come up in the course of my reading this past week. Consider Katherine Philips, the poetess, who was born in 1631. John Aubrey records of her that "She was when a Child much against the Bishops, and prayd to God to take them to him, but afterwards was reconciled to them. Prayed aloud, as the hypocriticall fashion then was, and was overheard." And then consider Edmund Gosse, as a Victorian child. When his father told him that he intended to marry again, and that the lady did not belong to the strict evangelistic sect of the Gosses, young Edmund, who was then eleven, shook a finger at him and said, "Papa, don't tell me that she's a paedobaptist?" He records that this affected his father painfully, as well it might. What modern child has the gumption or the learning for such an enquiry?

If the world is going to the dogs, it is the children's fault as much as anybody's. Sometimes I receive the impression that modern children are living solely for pleasure.

> Yours,
> Simon Goaste.

*

To Samuel Marchbanks, ESQ.

Dear Sam:

The other day I was looking at the Modern Library edition of Boswell's *Life of Dr. Samuel Johnson,* and in the Preface it was said that the inclusion of that book in that particular library of reprints awarded it "an accolade of modernity."

What a base passion our age has for pretending that whatever is good is necessarily "modern." What a depraved appetite we have for mere contemporaneity! How old Samuel Johnson would have snorted at the idea that a classic – particularly a classic about himself – was in some way ennobled by being declared the contemporary of the Wettums Doll, sliced, wrapped bread, and the singing telegram! This is an age without humility.

Your aggrieved
Amyas Pilgarlic.

＊

To the Rev. Simon Goaste, B.D.

Dear Pastor:

I have spent part of this week reading *The Great Divorce*, by C. S. Lewis. If you haven't read it, I recommend it as an excellent book about Heaven and Hell. But without illustrations. I feel that this is a real lack.

When I was a child there was in my home a strange book, the name of which I have forgotten, devoted to a detailed description of what evil-doers and worldly choosers might expect in the hereafter. It was bountifully and imaginatively illustrated with pictures of the damned being fried, grilled, toasted, fricasseed, barbecued, boiled and pressure-cooked by nimble little black devils with tails and disagreeable expressions. Since then I have read many speculations about Hell, including those of Dante, but none has impressed me so deeply. Another childhood book of mine was a Bible with Doré's illustrations including some which I think he made originally for *Paradise Lost*. And Doré's Devil will be my Devil forever – the humourless, malignant, infinitely sad winged creature; if we should ever meet he will not, I am sure, understand me at all, and to be misunderstood in Hell would be more terrible than to be understood through and through. This is a mighty persuasion to grace, and accounts for my lifelong circumspection.

Yours apprehensively,
Samuel Marchbanks.

＊

To Mervyn Noseigh, M.A.

Dear Mr. Noseigh:

I am enchanted by the thought that you wish to do a full-scale PH.D. thesis on my work. Of course I recognize your name immediately as that of the writer of essays already famous in the very littlest magazines:

Oh Marmee, What Big Teeth You Have: A Study of the pre-Oedipal mother in the works of Louisa May Alcott – (*Peewee Review*: Vol. 1, pp. 23-47)

Withering Depths: A Study of womb-frustration in Emily Bronte – (*Wee Wisdom*: Vol. 1, pp. 22-46)

Codnipped: A Study of impotence-fantasy in the adventure novels of Robert Louis Stevenson – (*Microscopic Quarterly*: Vol. 1, pp. 24-48).

These splendid studies are daily reading in the Marchbanks household. I cannot wait to see what you will make of me.

Tremulously yours,
Samuel Marchbanks.

*

To Amyas Pilgarlic, ESQ.

Dear Pil:

I had an enlightening experience yesterday, when I went to the exhibition of pictures at the Ontario Art Gallery with my friend Crosshatch, the artist. I had rather dreaded the visit, for Crosshatch knows a great deal about pictures: I know nothing of them. Crosshatch is widely admired for his taste: I am often told that my taste is all in my mouth. I am afraid of Crosshatch and shrink from displaying my ignorance when he is around.

When we entered the gallery, therefore, I was ready to put on an act as an Art Connoisseur. I had determined to pause for at least ninety seconds before every third picture, and to nod approvingly at least once in each room (but not at any special picture, for fear of showing ignorance). I reminded myself to stand at least eight feet from the pictures when looking at them, and to squint a lot, so as to look discerning. I worked up a little repertoire of remarks, such as "Interesting treatment," "Character there," "Nice feeling for colour," which I could murmur if Crosshatch liked a picture. I was loaded for bear when I entered the art gallery.

Judge of my amazement then, when Crosshatch whizzed around the rooms at a fast walk, neglecting whole wallfuls of pictures; he marched right up to others and glared at them, and tried the paint with a fingernail to see if it was dry; often he sniggered and sometimes he burst into a loud, derisive laugh; once he swore sharply, and made several people jump. We covered the show in half an hour flat, and he said, "Come on, let's get out of this," loudly enough for several obvious Art Lovers to hear him. But they whispered, "That's Crosshatch" in reverent voices, which seemed to make it all right.

Next time I go to an art show I shall know how to behave. Maybe somebody will mistake me for an artist.

Yours in the pride of enlightenment,
Sam.

*

To Haubergeon Hydra, ESQ.

Dear Mr. Hydra:

Enclosed find a cheque for $2.16; this, added to the $11.26 already deducted from my salary in weekly portions by my employers, completes the full sum of $13.42, the total of my Income Tax for the past year. It is also, if you care, almost an exact quarter of my yearly earnings, and I hope that you, as Deputy Confiscator-general, will take the utmost care of it.

Are you aware, sir, that when Captain Cook went to Australia in 1770 one of his men pointed to a kangaroo, and said, "What is it?" A native, standing by, said, "Kan g'aroo," meaning "I don't understand you." But the sailor thought that it was the name of the beast, and it has stuck to this day.

Now a similar error occurred when Jacques Cartier first set foot on the soil of our country. "What do you call this place?" he cried to a native. "Canada," cried the Indian in return, and Cartier took it for the country's name. But the Indian – one of the Crokinole tribe – actually said in the remarkably economical language of his people, "Take my advice, gentlemen, and go back where you came from; the taxes here are well-nigh insupportable." That is what Canada really means, but the time for turning back has passed.

And so, Mr. Hydra, as you press my $13.42 into the hand of a career diplomat who is going to fly round the world in order to see whether it is round or merely egg-shaped, or as you send it to a Western wheat-grower who needs it to enable him to go to California for the winter, remember how hard I had to work to earn it.

Yours maliciously and grudgingly,
Marchbanks the Tax-Serf.

*

A GARLAND OF MUSINGS

SACRED TO WHOM? / This evening I heard *The Rosary* (the work, if I recollect aright, of the ineffable Ethelbert Nevin) announced on the radio as a "sacred song." This caused me to laugh uproariously, for *The Rosary* is a love-song of a particularly gooey sort, in which the hours the lovers spent together are compared to rosary beads, and the final bust-up (probably when he deserted her for a girl who didn't wear her rosary to bed) to the embrace of the Cross. True lovers of the devotion of the rosary might fittingly shriek in protest every time this song is sung.

MONOTONY OF DIET / This evening to the movies and saw *Fabiola*, an Italian film about the goings-on of Christians under the Caesars – in this case the Emperor Constantine. It concluded with a grand mass martyrdom in which, at a rough guess, eight or ten thousand head of Christians were fed to a total count of six lions. Afterward I consulted Gibbon's *Decline and Fall of the Roman Empire*, in which he says he can find no record of more than ten Christians being turned off at a time, so I dismissed *Fabiola* as what Gibbon himself calls "holy romance." But the statistics and dietetics of the film still bother me, for even the most anti-clerical lion must weary of an unrelieved diet of Christians, consumed under circumstances of hustle and bustle.

THE RIDDLE OF THE SANDS / While I was away from home today a man brought a load of sand needed for some cement work; instead of dumping it where it was meant to be, he dropped it all in my driveway, making it impossible to put the car away. I presume that it is such thinking as this which makes sand truckers what they are, instead of eminent biologists, respected theologians, or the scented darlings of elegant boudoirs. With a heavy heart I set to work to heave the sand off the drive, and as it was wet I soon found that my heart was giving audible crunching sounds, as though somebody were crushing apples in my breast; my spine developed a hairpin bend and my knees shook; large black specks floated slowly before my eyes, my liver turned completely over, and bells tolled in my skull. The sand, however, was not without interest. In one shovelful I found what I believe is called a garter-belt. Who, I wondered, could have discarded her garter-belt in a sand pit, and why? Was I, all unwillingly, turning over the grave of some fleeting summer romance? And if so, was a sand pit not a somewhat gritty place for extra-mural amours? I shall never know. Crept into the house like a horse with the heaves, and took cordials suitable to my many ailments.

PRIMEVAL FILM / To the movies, to see Charlie Chaplin and Marie Dressler in *Tilly's Punctured Romance*, which they made in 1913. In my younger days I was an ardent follower of Charlie, but as I watched this relic from the Old Red Sandstone Period of the cinematic art, I realized that time had bathed the humour of another day in a golden but untruthful light. It was the most restless film I have seen in years. Nobody stood up if he could possibly fall down. Nobody fell down without at once leaping to his feet in order to fall down again. Nobody entered a door without slapping somebody else in the face with it. Food was never eaten, it existed only to be thrown. Liquid was not taken into the mouth in order to be swallowed, but only that it might be squirted into somebody else's face. The usual method of attracting a lady's attention was to kick her; she invariably responded with a blow. The life of man in the comedies of the silent films was solitary, poor, nasty, brutish and short. And viewed from this distance it does not appear to have been especially funny, at that.

*

CULLED FROM MY ARCHIVES

To Mrs. Kedijah Scissorbill.

Respected but Unloved Madam:

Walking along the street today I passed an organ-grinder; I gave him ten cents. I write to you of this because you are a dominating figure in many charities, and I often receive unpleasantly mimeographed, badly worded letters signed with a facsimile of your niggling signature, asking me for money. These letters always stress the deserving nature of the cause, and the care with which the money is administered by a staff of competent, well-paid officials. I usually respond to your letters with a donation, for your causes are genuinely good, and I am sure that you use the money wisely. Nevertheless, my heart does not go with them. My heart was with the organ-grinder's ten cents, even though he was unable to give me a slip entitling me to deduct my gift from taxable income.

Charity is infinitely better conducted nowadays than it was a century ago. It is thorough, economical, informed – everything but charitable. It does incalculable good to the receivers; it does nothing whatever to the givers – the answerers of form letters who never see the objects of their benevolence. For there is no merit in giving money, if one has it: the merit is in the charitable impulse and the cleansing of the spirit which compassion brings.

Modern charity is wonderful for the receivers, but it is useless to the givers. And I remind you that they also have souls to save. Charity is something greater than organized pillaging of the haves on behalf of the have-nots.

Yours with qualified approval,
Samuel Marchbanks.

*

To Raymond Cataplasm, M.D., F.R.C.P.

Dear Dr. Cataplasm:

At breakfast yesterday I watched a small boy sprinkle salt on his grapefruit. When I asked him about it, he said it made the fruit taste sweeter. A lady at the table said, "Mark my words, that child will die of hardening of the arteries." "Oh come, madam, surely that is an old wives' tale," said I. "Who are you calling an old wife," said she, and her wattles wobbled. "You," I rejoined, flicking a gob of marmalade at her and scampering from the room.

Tell me, Doctor, can salt harden the arteries? I have heard this threatened in connection with other household substances. For years I have followed each meal with a strong chaser of baking-soda and water, as an aid to digestion, and various people have told me that this will harden my arteries. Nevertheless my arteries are still capable of balloon-like expansion.

It seems to me that if anything were going to harden the arteries it would be excessive iron in the blood, which would coat the arteries with rust, like old hot-water pipes.

Your perennial patient and amateur adviser,
S. Marchbanks.

*

To Samuel Marchbanks, ESQ.

Honoured Sir:

Unexpected tidings, Mr. Marchbanks, sir. Your case against Richard Dandiprat will not come before the Autumn Assizes as we had planned. This is the result of a legal complication of a type incomprehensible to the lay mind, but I will try to explain it.

The papers in the case went, as usual, to Mr. Mouseman, Senior, for his consideration before they were taken to the court house. Knowing that the case would be tried before Mr. Justice Gripple – an old law-school companion of Mr. Mouseman's – he made a pencilled notation on the document giving notice of the case, which said: "Don't let this come up any day when Old Gripple has lost heavily at bridge the night before. You know that he really needs a murder or a rape case on such days as a relief for his spleen." This was intended as a private direction to the sheriff, but some foolish clerk transcribed it on a document which reached Mr. Justice Gripple himself. He said several things which convinced our firm that it would be better to ask for a delay, and bring the case up again in the Spring, when we are confident that Mr. Justice Gripple will be in another part of the Province.

Oh, the law, the law! What a fascinating study it is, Mr. Marchbanks. You laymen cannot comprehend the subtle psychological elements which may sway the judgement of the courts! But patience – patience must be the watchword of the successful litigant.

Yours with infinite patience,
Mordecai Mouseman
(for Mouseman, Mouseman and Forcemeat).

*

To Mervyn Noseigh, M.A.

Dear Mr. Noseigh:

I am overjoyed by the news that you have really decided to do a PH.D. thesis on my work, and am especially tickled by your title – *Skunk's Misery to Toronto: a study of spiritual degeneration in the work of Samuel Marchbanks.* The questions you ask fill me with delightful new importance. Number 7 (a) for example: "What were the first books you remember reading and what influence do you consider that they have had on your later style and symbological system?"

The first books I remember reading were called *Mother Hubbard's House Party,* and *Chuck and Cooney Caught in the Corn;* the first of these was about a Christmas party assembled by Mother Hubbard (a kind of Magna Mater or Demeter-figure, as I now realize) at which Jack and Jill, Mary Mary Quite Contrary, Tom Tom the Piper's Son, Georgy Porgy, Little Jack Horner and Little BoPeep acted out, in a high mimesis, various pseudo-Arcadian romances, culminating in a mass bedding at the end of the day. Although the writer had badly botched this conclusion, I assume that the Primal Scene was enacted by all these characters in turn, in every conceivable combination, under the obscene prompting of Mother Hubbard, who had assumed a Hecate-identity with the coming of darkness. I now realize that the book was a pseudonymous work by Frank Harris.

As for Chuck and Cooney, they appeared to be a wood-chuck and a raccoon who were surprised by a farmer in his corncrib, and escaped by a narrow margin, but I am aware that it was a thinly-disguised fable of race-hatred, because Cooney was the stupid one and got into all the serious trouble.

All my subsequent work has drawn heavily on these sources, accounting for the ugly undertone on which you comment so frankly. Please tell me more. There is nothing that flatters an author so much as having his work explained to him by a graduate student who brings a modern, critically-trained intellect to bear upon it. I can hardly wait for the next instalment.

Eagerly yours,
Samuel Marchbanks.

*

FROM MY NOTEBOOKS

STRANGE DELUSION / Waiting to see my doctor today I fell into conversation with a woman, obviously from the country, who sat near me. She appeared to be deeply aggrieved at life in general, though her manner was pleasant enough, and I judged that she was suffering from some inconvenient but not serious malady. "You city people don't know how well off you are," she said, broodingly. "Every kind of convenience – electric toilets and such." I marvelled at the quaintness of this idea, but did not feel capable of explaining the limitations of hydro-electric power to her. But since then I have gazed at the plumbing at Marchbanks Towers with new eyes.

FOG-DENSITY / Picked up a magazine this afternoon and read an article by a man who had appointed himself an expert upon what he called the "fog-density" of authors – meaning the difficulty which they presented to the average reader. He did not reveal all his secrets, but one way in which he measures this quality is to count the number of three-syllable words in every 100 words of a writer's prose. If they are frequent, fog-density is high. I suppose I present a considerable fog-density to some of my readers, but I don't care; who wants to be understood by everybody? I like long and unusual words, and anybody who does not share my taste is not compelled to read me. Policemen and politicians are under some obligation to make themselves comprehensible to the intellectually stunted, but not I. Let my prose be tenebrous and rebarbative; let my pennyworth of thought be muffled in gorgeous apparel; lovers of Basic English will look to me in vain.

LET US BE PATIENT / The failure of yet another Canadian play on Broadway was attributed to many things, but I think it was owing to the simple fact that nobody is interested in Canadians except, very occasionally, other Canadians. Nations enjoy spells of popularity in the theatre and elsewhere; they become fashionable for no reason that I can discover. For centuries, for instance, nobody was interested in Scotsmen; they were regarded simply as hairy fellows who spoke faulty English. But during the nineteenth century plays about Scots, books about them, jokes about them and indeed everything about them sprang into a new popularity. We are beginning to tire of them now, but Irishmen, Armenians, and Scandinavians have become objects of popular interest. As yet the world does not think that Canadians are interesting; we stand where the Scotch stood before the Big Bagpipe Boom of the Victorian Era, and the period of 1900-1920, when Sir James Barrie persuaded the world that, appearances to the contrary, all Scots were delightful fellows with the souls of little children. Canada's day will come, no doubt, but we may have to wait a few centuries for it.

SABBATH MUSINGS / Sat by my window, and as the church bells rang and people hastened past my door with their prayerbooks and hymnals in their hands, I pondered upon the secrets of the human heart. Do people go to church in Chalk River, I wondered, and in Los Alamos? And if they do so, do they try to square it with the Almighty that they are engaged in making the most devilish engines of destruction that the world has ever known? We are assured, of course, that atomic power will do great things for the world at peace, but we never hear anything specific except what it will do for the world at war. Do the wives of atomic scientists worry about hats and social prestige? Did the wife of Dr. Faustus fret about what to do with the leftovers of yesterday's dinner while the Doctor was in his study chatting with the Devil? The answer to all these questions, I have no doubt, is Yes.

CARELESS MUSICIAN / Joined in a private sing-song – one of those affairs where three or four people work through a book called *The Jumbo Volume of Songs the Whole World Loves*, or something of the kind. We sang *The Lost Chord*, familiar to me as a boy through a gramophone record of Arthur Pryor playing it on the trombone. But, as I sang, I wondered how the musician in the song ever lost that chord, which sounded like a great Amen? I am no master of musical theory, but the number of chords on an organ which could have sounded like a great Amen to a Victorian organist were remarkably few, and if he was unable to find it again the Royal College of Organists should have insisted that he repeat his final examinations.

GOGOL UNMASKED / Was talking to a Russian, and worked up courage to address him thus: "For many years I have read in books about literature that the Russian author Nikolai Gogol was a very great humorist – the peer of Shakespeare, Aristophanes and Cervantes – and that his novel *Dead Souls* is one of the world's great funny books. During a bout of 'flu last year I read *Dead Souls* carefully, attentively and receptively, but my gravity was not disturbed. Am I stupid, or does Gogol not translate well into English, or what is the matter?" (During this I took care to pronounce Gogol's name in a gargling fashion, which I hoped would sound Russian.) To my amazement he replied: "My dear Samuel Marchbankovitch, I have never thought Gogol very funny myself. Indeed, Russian writers are never funny in the way that English or American writers are. They are rather facetious, little father, but that is all." (I observed that he pronounced the name "Goggle," which I take to be the true Russian manner.) So there it is. I suppose that the Russians, like every other nation, like to pretend that they have a sense of humour. I have been told Chinese jokes, too, by people who thought them funny though, like much Chinese art, the only interesting thing about them was that they were Chinese.

CANADIAN SHIBBOLETH / Was at a party where a merry fellow – a Ph.D. and much respected in academic circles – was tormenting an Australian lady about the accent he believed to be characteristic of her native land. "I can always tell an Aussie by the way they say 'stewed fruit,'" he declared, and then went on saying "stewed fruit" very comically, as well as he could through his laughter. "Please say 'wash and curl the hair of the squirrel,'" said the Australian lady, and the savant obligingly said, "Worsh 'n currl the haira the squrrl." "That is how I always know a Canadian," said she, and he was not pleased. But there is something about a Canadian which compels him, however much education and sophistication he may have attained in other realms, to preserve intact the accent in which his barefoot old granny used to curse the timber wolves that raged around her cabin. It is one of the last areas in which illiteracy is equated with integrity.

*

COMMUNIQUÉ (*dropped down my chimney*)

To Big Chief Marchbanks.

How, Marchbanks:
    Meet fellow on park bench yesterday. Bum, Marchbanks. He awful fat. I got to get rid of this fat, he say. Why, I say. Fat not healthy, he say. All doctors say fat make you die young. First I got to get money to eat, he say, then I got to go on diet. You got fat head, I say. Look at bear. Bear awful fat. Bear

healthy, too. Bear healthier than any doctor. Skinny doctor meet fat bear, bear win every time. You poor ignorant Indian, he say. You know nothing about modern science. I know bears, I say.

Not in jail yet, Marchbanks. Winter come soon. How can I get in jail?

How, again,
>   Osceola Thunderbelly,
>   Chief of the Crokinoles.

*

CULLED FROM THE APOPHTHEGMS
OF WIZARD MARCHBANKS

A book is criticized by the reviewer in direct proportion as the reviewer is criticized by the book: no man can find wisdom in print which is not already waiting for words within himself.

Mercury

Virgo

mutable, earthy

Samuel Marchbanks b. Aug. 28 & thus astrological sibling of Goethe & Tolstoy; birth attended by portents in the heavens — first noted UFOs.

(August 24 to September 23)

VIRGO IS the sign of the Virgin, and those born under it have a special gift of emerging from the most dishevelled situations looking as though butter wouldn't melt in their mouths. You who are born under this sign will do well to take fullest advantage of your air of inexperience and untouchability which, with careful husbanding, should last all your life, deluding thousands of people, some of whom ought to know better. Staggering as the notion is, all astrologers agree that the greatest danger to you lies in over-work; therefore you should never lose an opportunity to rest, and should always put off until tomorrow what people born under Leo have demanded that you do today.

Enchantment-of-the-Month

↓☺↑↓☺↑*↓☺↑*↓☺↑*↓☺↑*↓☺↑

As you might have expected, those born under the sign of Virgo have a somewhat cool group of lucky colours – green, greeny-yellowy, blue and black. Your lucky flowers likewise are on the quiet side – bachelor's button, mourning bride, lavender and azalea. Your lucky stones are marcasite (or white iron pyrites if you want to drag the thing down to its lowest level), agate (of the kind from which children's marbles are made), jasper and the more attractive emerald and topaz. You will probably wonder why those born under the sign of the Virgin are not encouraged to wear white. I do not know, but I think you should be pleased that you have been spared such a trying colour; it is a nuisance to maintain and very few people look really well in it. Also, it is a ridiculous colour for men. The only man in recent history who habitually wore white clothes was Mark Twain, who was born under Sagittarius and should have worn black, both for astrological and laundry considerations.

Health Hints for Those Born Under Virgo

Disagreeable as such a revelation must be to the Virgin-born, your weak spot is your intestines, and astrologers for five centuries have advised your kind to keep away from rich foods and sweetmeats. Your liver, spleen, pancreas and tripes are all of a delicate and readily incommoded disposition. Much of your pensive and romantic character in youth springs directly from this source, but as middle age overtakes you these qualities are likely to be transformed into simple dyspepsia. It is then that you must either behave like a philosopher and eat a restricted and moderate diet, or embark on a life of alternating excess and remorse – the Christmas Dinner followed by the Awful Session in the Night. Many of the Virgo-born attempt to sublimate their dyspepsia – to render it nobler by pretending that it is some mysterious and debilitating complaint which they bear with a martyr's smile – but this rarely works. The eructation and the borborygmy, the yellow eyeball and the pallid cheek betray too plainly where the trouble really lies.

*

INVENTOR OF THE HANDKERCHIEF / I should like to learn something every day, but whole months pass during which I learn nothing at all. Today, however, a crumb of information came my way which I had never nibbled before, and it was this: the handkerchief was invented by King Richard II. He was the first man known to history to carry a piece of linen or silk, clean every day, for blowing his nose. This seems to me to raise Richard to a higher place in the ranks of English royalty than he is usually granted. We make a hero of Henry V, who was a loud-mouthed brawler, and we take an indulgent view of his father, Henry IV, who was a crook. Both of these fellows, though usurpers of Richard's throne, blew their noses on their fingers and slept in their underwear. But Richard, who invented the handkerchief and seems to have been one of the very few English politicians who knew how to get along with the Irish, is usually brushed off as a foolish fellow who liked poetry and music, attended plays and wasted money on triflers like Chaucer. For his invention of the handkerchief I insist that he deserves a statue in pure gold.

CHURCH ECONOMICS / Attended an entertainment in a church hall this evening, and during the intervals some little girls sold fudge in aid of their Sunday School. They handed over a large sack of first-class fudge in return for ten cents, and this struck me as typical church economics, for there was at least twenty cents' worth of delicious fattening sweetmeat in each bag. If these little girls had business instincts, they would reckon their over-head, time, cartage to the church, and materials, and would then sell the fudge at thirty-five cents a bag; but as no one could then afford to eat it, they would lobby for a government subsidy, which would pay them twenty cents on each bag of fudge, allowing them to sell for fifteen cents. As the fudge would still sell very well at that price, there would soon be a glutted market, and they would get the government to buy their surplus fudge at the full retail price, and sell it to Europe for ten cents a bag. However, I did not explain these things to them, but contented myself with buying two bags of bargain fudge, and stealing another, which somebody, in the seats in front of mine, left behind them at the end of the entertainment.

*

*

FROM MY FILES

To the Rev. Simon Goaste, B.D.

Dear Rector:

   Do you believe in reincarnation? I don't suppose you do,
and neither do I, but it is attractive nonsense, none the less. I ask
because it occurred to me last night that I might possibly be a
reincarnation of Good Queen Bess. I read that she "passionately
admired handsome persons and he was already far advanced in
her favour who approached her with beauty and grace. She had
so unconquerable an aversion for men who had been treated unfortunately by nature, that she could not endure their presence."
I feel just the same. I like handsome people, particularly women.
I also like people who are fascinatingly ugly. It's the in-betweens
who give me eye-strain and I generally treat them with bad-
tempered indifference.

   So perhaps I am Queen Elizabeth returned to earth. Have
you noticed that people who believe in reincarnation never
imagine that they were a person of no importance in another
life? Have you ever heard one claim that he was a slave who
worked quite contentedly on the Pyramids, and died of rupture
at 23? Or that he was a peasant who neglected to go to see Joan
of Arc burned because he was mending his roof? Or that he was
a Scottish crofter who saw young James Watt watching the
tea-kettle and said "Yon laddie'll never amount to owt"? But the
world is full of unrecognized Napoleons, Cleopatras and similar
great ones.

   Yours sincerely,
      Samuel Marchbanks
      (or possibly Queen Elizabeth).

*

To Miss Nancy Frisgig.

Charming Nancy:

   I have your note in which you say that you wish you had
lived in the Middle Ages, because it must have been such fun.
I'm not so sure. Do you know that during the greater part of
what we call the Middle Ages nobody had a bed? They slept on
heaps of straw, quite naked, and it was considered pernickety to
change the straw more than two or three times a year. Those
who had beds slept in curious contrivances which caused them
to lie at an angle of forty-five degrees; it must have been rather
like sleeping standing up. Do you know that there were no
chimneys in those times? Fires were built in the middle of the

main room of the house, and the smoke escaped through a hole in the roof, but only after it had whirled all around the room and choked everybody. When, late in the Middle Ages, chimneys were introduced, they caused outraged complaint among architectural critics and moralists who thought discomfort must be healthy.

But the real trial was the music. Last week I had a chance to hear quite a lot of mediaeval music, played on a lute, by a modern expert. I suppose you think of a lute as a charming instrument which young men would have played under your window to show that they loved you? Ha, ha. The lute sounds pretty much like a guitar with a cold in its head. A catarrh, in fact. Ho, ho.

So when you are tempted to idealize the Middle Ages, imagine yourself lying naked in dirty, tickly straw, breathing smoke and listening to the lute. There is really a great deal to be said for modern comfort.

Yours as always,
    Sam.

    *

To Haubergeon Hydra, ESQ.

My dear Mr. Hydra:

I am not an unreasonable man, I hope, but the Government's action in bringing in Daylight Saving, or Summer Time, has caused me a degree of inconvenience which rouses me to protest. And naturally it is to you, as Deputy Commissioner of Officially Approved Nuisances, that I turn.

The principal timepiece in my home, sir, is a striking clock. At the half hour it goes Dong, and at the hour it goes Dong as many times as it is o'clock. Or rather, I should say that it goes Whang, for the thing in its intestines which makes the noise is not a bell, but a coiled spring, which simulates the sound of a bell less than perfectly.

Now some years ago this clock fell ill of a horological malady which caused its Whanging apparatus to lose an hour, so that it always Whangs one too few. And now that you have further complicated matters with your Daylight Saving, it Whangs two too few, which is more than flesh and blood can bear, particularly when it Whangs midnight at two a.m.

As you know, it is fatal to tamper with a good clock. One must take it as it is, or not at all. But my clock is unnerving me, and I hold you and the Government responsible.

Yours at sixes and sevens,
    Samuel Marchbanks.

    *

To Raymond Cataplasm, M.D., F.R.C.P.

Dear Dr. Cataplasm:

Cannot the medical profession do anything about the vast quantity of medical misinformation which is foisted upon the public under the guise of beauty hints? I am just as anxious to be beautiful as anyone, and I read in a magazine yesterday that it was a very good thing to lie down for half an hour with your feet higher than your head. The writer stated flatly that this would relieve bags under the eyes, blotchy complexion, sinus trouble, slumped abdomen, *taedium vitae* and all the other ills from which I suffer. So I tried it.

It was not positively unpleasant, though it produced an effect rather like slow strangulation. The article led me to believe that this was wonderful fresh blood swirling around in my blood-starved brain. But when the half hour was up, and I rose to my feet, everything about me which had been slumped before slumped again with such sudden force that for a moment I thought the shock would bear me to the ground. I was just able to stagger to a sofa, and lie down in a perfectly horizontal position until the fit had passed.

My beauty has not been noticeably enhanced by this experience. Why are such impostures permitted?

Yours in a condition of utter slump,
Samuel Marchbanks.

*

To Amyas Pilgarlic, ESQ.

Dear Pil:

It is a bit thick, your rebuke to me for believing in ghosts, calling them "superstitions unbecoming a scientific age." If there is one lesson science impresses on us all, it is surely that *nothing* is incredible.

Haven't you heard about "neutrinos"? Apparently there are such things — little doodads of which *sixty billion* penetrate each square inch of our bodies *every second* and go on their way having done no harm whatever. But nobody has so far suggested that the neutrinos are, in their way, unaware of us. I put it to you that to a neutrino you and I probably seem like ghosts. And I put it to you also that we may, in our turn, be as neutrinos to other beings, whizzing in and about them without much awareness, but with an occasional intuition that things are not quite as simple as even our five wits lead us to suppose.

Multiply my bulk in square inches by sixty billion, and reflect that it is from amid that assemblage of unknown but active creatures that I now adjure you to bethink yourself, and stop talking nonsense. We are all much more ghostly than we know.

Your eerie comrade,
Samuel Marchbanks.

*

A GARLAND OF MUSINGS

TECHNICOLOUR FLAUBERT / Picked up Gustave Flaubert's *Salammbo*, a book which I read as a schoolboy and looked upon with wry smiles even then, as it appears to me to be written in Technicolour; however, as I read it in translation I would be wise to keep quiet, for any Frenchman can shout me down. But the tone of the book is exhausting; nobody ever says "Giddap" to a horse; they always "urge it forward with a hoarse cry." Nobody looks at a woman; he devours her with his eyes. I prefer a quieter life. . . . *Salammbo* suggests that medical practice in ancient Carthage was on an equally irrational footing with war and the pursuit of love. One remedy which is described is "the blood of a black dog slaughtered by barren women on a winter's night among the ruins of a tomb"; a druggist who had filled a few prescriptions like that in the course of a day might well think of going into some other business. . . . However, *Salammbo* is enthralling, in its strange way, and I read it for half an hour after lunch before I realized that I had work to do, and urged myself toward my desk with a hoarse cry, devouring several women with my eyes as I trudged through the snow. One of them was eying a black dog reflectively, and I concluded that she was at least on the Pill.

A MEAGRE DIET / For several weeks I have been following a diet prescribed by my physician, which includes a great deal of seafood. Yet I find that when I order lobster or jumbo shrimps at a meal, and explain that I must mind my diet, the people with whom I am eating snigger in an underbred fashion and hint that I am a luxurious rascal, and that my diet is a thing of the imagination. This is bitterly unjust, but I do not know what I am to do about it. I like seafood, and eat it with obvious relish; is it necessary that everything on a diet should be nasty? I don't like spinach and broccoli, but I eat them, and get no pity for it. Why am I grudged a simple little thing like a lobster or a dozen oysters?

CHILDREN AND CERAMICS / Attended a little party where there was a type of pickle hitherto unknown to me, though I consider myself rather an expert on pickles. It was made of infant ears of corn, an inch or two long, preserved in some savoury embalming fluid; they were delicious. But as I looked at these tiny ears, plucked before they had grown to fullness and maturity, and arrested in their growth for our delight, I was strongly reminded of those children who, during the Middle Ages, were turned into dwarfs for the pleasure of people whose income permitted them to run to the luxury of a household dwarf. Gypsies kidnapped these children and encased them in pottery forms, so that they could not grow, and developed into wry shapes, regarded as funny by our strong-stomached ancestors. When they had reached adult years, the pottery form was broken, and there was a child, of a kind, with an adult mind, of a kind. I do not suppose this curious trade will ever be revived. I have watched some of the pottery classes sponsored by our recreational associations, but I have never seen anybody at work on a pot which suggested that it was for the jugging of a child.

*

FROM MY ARCHIVES

To Raymond Cataplasm, M.D., F.R.C.P.

Dear Dr. Cataplasm:

I see that an eminent member of your profession has declared that in his opinion sleep was the original and natural state of all living things. The lower organisms still exist, says he, in a somnolent condition: great numbers of higher creatures pass months every year in hibernation – which is a kind of sleep: the most sleepless of all is the king of them all – Man, proud Man. He suggests that we might be better off if we slept more. But it seems to me that it might be argued to the contrary that we should be even more civilized if we slept less.

I write to you from a transcontinental train, upon which I am hastening toward our great Canadian West. As I bump and clatter across the broad and lumpy bosom of our motherland I find it impossible to sleep at all. Other people sleep, but not Marchbanks, the super-civilized. My eyelids feel as though someone had been striking matches on them, and when I push them down over the peeled grapes swimming in stewed rhubarb which are my eyes, hot balls of pain bounce around in my head.

But am I more civilized than in the days when I slept for the usual eight hours? I am certainly more fearful, jumpy and cross-grained, and these are the badges of civilization today. When I return, I want you to give me some medicine to uncivilize me. A barbiturate to make me barbarous, shall we say?

Your unbearably civilized patient,
Samuel Marchbanks.

*

To Amyas Pilgarlic, ESQ.

Dear Pil:

Yesterday I was in Banff and its mountainous environs. Have you ever thought how romantically some mountains are named? The Three Sisters, for instance. If I had been asked to name it I should have called it The Three Jagged Snags, or, in a more poetic vein, The Hag's Lower Denture. But no: The Three Sisters it is. There are cases, of course, where the names are well chosen. Several mountains are named after millionaires and bankers, and they have just the right unapproachable, frosty look. One is named after a missionary: it has a look of suspicious disapproval like the banker-mountains, but on a more spiritual plane, if I make myself clear. I like mountains, but I refuse to be patronized by them.

What really astonishes me here in the West is the superstitious awe which is extended toward the East. Whenever Westerners are behaving in a natural and jolly manner, somebody is likely to say, "Of course, we know you don't carry on like this in the East." It is rather a new thing for me to be in a place where Ontario is regarded as a gentle, old-world, tradition-encrusted civilization, but I suppose I shall get used to it. Indeed I am doing so right here in Banff. I am older than the rocks among which I sit, and my eyelids are a little weary. I am beginning to take pride in certain gracious old Ontario traditions, such as wearing a neck-tie in the morning and depending on braces instead of a belt. I have not, as some Easterners do, bought myself a white cowboy hat. Something – a life-long mistrust of cows, perhaps, and a conviction that their milk is the most over-rated drink known to man – prevents me. Tomorrow I press on dauntlessly to Vancouver.

Yours,
Sam.

*

To Waghorn Wittol, ESQ.

Dear Wittol:

When I was at Banff yesterday my guide showed me, with utmost pride, a big heap of sticks, mud and dirt which was, he said, a beaver lodge.

In fact, it was undistinguishable from the big heap of sticks, mud and dirt behind the garage at Marchbanks Towers. I have been trying to get a man to come and haul this away, but I shall not do so now. If anyone asks me what it is I shall say airily, "Oh, a beaver lodge." The word rubbish will not be uttered in its presence. – How travel broadens one's outlook.

My regards to Mrs. Wittol, if you can find her.

Samuel Marchbanks.

*

To Haubergeon Hydra, ESQ.

Dear Mr. Hydra:

As a citizen and taxpayer of this country I write to you, as Deputy Guarantor of Tourist Attractions, to complain about our prairies: they are not as flat as I was led to believe. People have assured me for years that the prairie is as flat as a billiard table. This, sir, is a lie put out to attract tourists. It is not nearly so flat as that.

There is much talk of conservation these days, but very little action. Let us not lose our prairies. Tear down the farmhouses at once: nobody wants them: the farmers are all in California spending their wheat subsidy. And then put a fleet of steam rollers on the prairies and get those unsightly humps out of them. Keep at it until they are, as advertised, flat as a billiard table.

Your indignant taxpayer,

S. Marchbanks.

*

To Amyas Pilgarlic, ESQ.

Dear Pil:

Since last I wrote to you I have gone through what is widely believed to be one of the most moving spiritual experiences a Canadian can sustain – a jaunt through the Rocky Mountains. I enjoyed it, but spiritually I am exactly where I was before. I have seen them in full sunlight, which robs them of all mystery, and I have seen them in a rainy haze, which is much better. I have gaped at chunks of rock which are said to resemble the faces of Indians, though the likeness escaped me. I have looked shudderingly down into gorges over which the train was passing. I have been pleased, diverted and surprised, but I am not one of those who finds a sight of the Rockies an equivalent for getting religion at a revival meeting.

To make a shameful confession, the Rockies put me in mind of nothing so much as the first act of *Rose Marie,* a musical comedy of my younger days and the favourite theatre entertainment of his late Majesty, King George V. At any moment I expected a lovely French-Canadian girl to leap on the observation car, saying, "You make ze marriage wiz me, no?" Or an Indian girl, more lithe and beautiful than any Indian girl has ever been, to begin a totem dance on the track. The scenery was right: only the actors were missing.

Upon arrival in Vancouver, the first thing to meet my eye was a notice, signed by the Chief of Police, warning me against confidence tricksters. It told me in detail how I might expect them to work. I would be approached, first of all, by someone who would try to make friends: this would be "The Steerer" who would eventually steer me to "The Spieler," who would sell me Stanley Park or the harbour at a bargain price. Not long after I had read this I was approached by a crafty-looking woman carrying a handful of pasteboards. "Juwanna buy four chances on the Legion car?" she cried, blocking my way. "Madam, you are wasting your time," said I; "I know you for what you are – a Steerer." She shrank away, muttering unpleasantly. Never let it be said that Marchbanks failed to heed a warning.

Vancouver has much to recommend it as a city; indeed, if it were not on the other side of those pestilent mountains I should go there often. Among other attractions it has a large and interesting Chinese quarter, where I ate the best Chinese food I have ever tasted. There are times when I think that I shall give up Occidental cuisine altogether, and eat Chinese food for the rest of my life. After lunch I wandered among the Chinese shops, and found one which sold a scent called "Girl Brand Florida Water." There is a simplicity about that name which enchants me. In the same shop I saw the only piece of Chinese nude art that has ever come my way; the Chinese are believed not to care for representations of the nude: but this was plainly the result of Western influence; it was a Chinese girl, lightly draped, holding aloft a bunch of paper flowers. Her legs were short, her body long, and she seemed more amply endowed for sitting than Western standards of beauty permit. It was, I suppose, the kind of thing one finds in Chinese bachelor apartments, just as Occidental bachelors enrich their rooms with ash-trays held aloft by naked beauties in chrome, and drink beer from glasses into which libidinous pictures have been etched. East is East, and West is West, but bachelors are wistful rascals the world over.

Normally I do not mind cigars. I smoke them myself. But on a train – ! Opposite me as I write sits a little bald man with a baby face and a head like a peeled onion who has, for the past 45 minutes, burned and sucked the most villainous stogie I have ever choked over. He has doused it with his drool, and re-lit it, five several times. He is just about to do so again and I must leave him to it, or strike him with the emergency axe, or be sick myself. If he made that stench by any other means, the sanitary inspector would condemn him.

Yours gaggingly,
Sam.

*

FROM MY NOTEBOOKS

WHERE AM I? / Was driving through the countryside today with some people who insisted upon frequent recourse to a road-map in order to discover, as they put it, "Just where they were." Reflected that for my part I generally have a pretty shrewd idea of just where I am; I am enclosed in the somewhat vulnerable fortress which is my body, and from that uneasy stronghold I make such sorties as I deem advisable into the realm about me. These people seemed to think that whizzing through space in a car really altered the universe for them, but they were wrong; each one remained right in the centre of his private universe, which is the only field of knowledge of which he has any direct experience.

DE GUSTIBUS LOTS OF DISPUTANDUM / Had a pleasant chat with Dr. Boyd Neel, the conductor of the celebrated chamber orchestra. I asked him if he meant to play any contemporary music while he was touring Canada. "Oh yes," said he, "I expect we may play a few new tunes." This reply delighted me, for I am sick of the cloud of mystery and fear which surrounds modern music. It is not all harsh to the ear – to any ear, that is, which does not regard the barrel-organ as the last word in harmony – and much of it is very jolly and enlivening. There are even tunes in some recent pieces, though not tunes that you can whistle. I strongly suspect that it is hard work to write a tune if you set your face against the aids of folk-song and the forthright spirit of the Salvation Army Band. But I admired Dr. Neel because he spoke of modern music without passion. I grow weary of those people who become super-charged at the mention of modern music, or modern poetry, or modern painting; these are topics of great interest, but why must one be expected to take sides, violently for or against? "There is no disputing about tastes," says the old saw. In my experience there is little else.

NON-STOP CULTURE / A man was exulting to me today about the wonders of a gramophone which he had given to himself and his family at Christmas. The beauty of it, in his eyes, is that it will play for eight hours without a stop, and he can heap four or five symphonies on it and let them rip. Ah, well; each to his pleasure. I find one symphony about all I can cope with in a day; my emotional blood-pressure rises sharply if too much passionate symphonic music is forced upon me in a single dose. Anyway, I don't like to have a huge orchestra roaring in my living-room when I am trying to rest. For the chamber, chamber music is the proper fare.

AN ILLUSION SHATTERED / Was in the country today, and coming over the crest of a hill was surprised to see a fox a few yards away; it did not see me, and the wind was in the wrong direction for it to scent me, so I watched it for what seemed a long time, but was probably two minutes. Then it turned, saw me, gazed for a few seconds, and trotted away grinning. This is not what I would have expected, and when I returned to town I called a naturalist friend and told him that the fox had not appeared to be afraid of me. "Oh no," he said, "unless you shot at it, or shouted, it probably wouldn't fear you; foxes are stupid creatures – any dog is smarter than any fox – and if it couldn't scent you it probably didn't realize even that you were a man." This was a blow to the notion I acquired as a child, from countless stories, that foxes are brilliantly intelligent, and the master-minds of the forest world. And after all, what evidence have we that a fox is clever? When chased it runs away, and makes better time in country it knows than a dog does. Is that clever? But a fox looks clever, and with animals as with humans, that is more than half the battle.

*

TELLING FORTUNES BY MOLES
(*a bonus for readers of the Almanack*)

There are many ways of telling fortunes, and no *Almanack* is complete without some allusion to at least one of them: Palmistry is the favourite, but it has been done to death; anyhow, it is hard to learn and there are too many people whose hand-lines do not conform to any known pattern. Therefore Wizard Marchbanks will confine himself to *Fortune Telling by Moles*, which is easy and rather dashing. Of course, there are people who are sensitive about their moles, and you had better avoid them. Here are the five easily memorized rules which will enable you to practise this fascinating branch of White Magic.

Moles on the Face: if extremely numerous and whimsically placed, the subject is likely to be unlucky in love.

Moles on the Arms: do not really count.

Moles on the Legs: should not be alluded to if the fortune-teller is desirous of the continued acquaintance of his subject.

Moles on the Back: are usually visible only when evening dress is worn and should not be mentioned.

Moles Elsewhere: are rarely disclosed until the immediate future of both subject and fortune-teller is easily predictable anyhow.

＊

COMMUNIQUÉ (*shot through my window attached to an arrow*)

To Big Chief Marchbanks.

How, Marchbanks:

Good news, Marchbanks, I in jail now. Last week I try awful hard to get in jail. I throw brick at cop. He just wag finger and laugh. I call insult at mayor. He just lift hat. Getting near election time, Marchbanks. I write dirty word on City Hall. City Clerk come out and write "Ditto," under it. No hope, Marchbanks. Then one day cop look at me very queer. You pay your poll tax, he ask. No, I say, I never own no pole. Aha, he say, you got to pay poll tax. I never have no totem pole, I say. Sell 'um to tourist twenty year ago. Come along, he say, and we go to court. They find I owe $3,000 back poll tax. Put me in jail. Ha ha. That great tax, Marchbanks. Friendly tax to poor Indian. All set for winter now. You got money? I not need money.

How, again,
Osceola Thunderbelly,
Chief of the Crokinoles.

＊

CULLED FROM THE APOPHTHEGMS
OF WIZARD MARCHBANKS

Prophecy consists of carefully bathing the inevitable in the eerie light of the impossible, and then being the first to announce it.

Libra

Venus

an airy sign

legal firm of Mouseman,
Mouseman & Forcemeat
founded Sept. 25, 1810

the fallen state of Man. A soul or embarking in this world may forget the perfect love in...

(September 24 to October 23)

LIBRA IS the sign of the Scales, and those born under this sign are noted for their tendency to balance one thing against another. This characteristic is not understood by persons born under less subtle signs and they may sometimes accuse you of trying to eat your cake and have it too. You may comfort yourself with the knowledge that they would do the same if they knew how. Your passion for symmetry extends to every sphere of life; an eye for an eye and a tooth for a tooth is the law of the Libra-born, and "getting even" is absolutely necessary to those with such a nicely balanced temperament. In order that this dominant trait in your character may have fullest scope, you would do well to embrace such professions as the law or the civil service, in which society will recognize and support your desire to arrange things to suit yourself. You are not moved by an ugly desire to overreach your fellow-man; you are simply determined to keep level with him at

113 *

all times, and as people born under other signs are usually losers in some of the encounters of life you, the Libra-born, must not be surprised if, on the average, you come out a little ahead of everyone else.

Enchantment-of-the-Month
*✦⚬✦✦⚬✦✦⚬✦✦⚬✦✦⚬✦✦⚬✦

Your lucky colours are white, yellow and blue. Your lucky flowers are foxglove, violet, daisy and lily-of-the-valley. Your lucky gems are the moonstone, sapphire, opal, beryl and coral. These are trivial considerations, however, when compared with the long-established astrological fact that women born under Libra are exceptionally lucky in love. Do not trade too heavily on this; do not assume that whatever you do, you can't go wrong. But if you use ordinary gumption, you have a better chance than most girls of having a few recollections to whisper to your grandchildren when your children are out of the room. This particular kind of good fortune does not extend to Libra men; their success lies in trades which mean delving in the earth – mining, plumbing and grave-digging. Whether this latter good fortune extends to the higher flights of the mortician's art is a question for which Wizard Marchbanks has not yet been able to wring an answer from the stars.

Health Hints for Those Born Under Libra

The sign under which you were born disposes you to almost any ailment which strikes below the belt. Your kidneys, lower abdomen, lumbar region and knees are your weak points. Though in general full of advice on matters relating to health, Wizard Marchbanks confesses himself stumped by this situation. and is inclined to tell you to wear flannel drawers and hope for the best. However, it was not for such offhand advice that you bought this book. Therefore it is suggested that you collect a good mixture of herbs – any well-known herbs will do – and brew them into a strong tea; drink freely of this whenever you feel out of sorts. If you feel ill, the herbs will certainly make you feel worse; when this feeling passes the improvement will encourage you and may even bring you back to perfect health, out of sheer relief.

*

COMMUNIQUÉ (*delivered by carrion crow*)

To Big Chief Marchbanks.

How, Marchbanks:

Everybody in jail crazy, Marchbanks. Jail doctor bring old white squaw see us jail prisoners today. She squint at me through glasses. You got any sociable diseases, she say. Sure, I say. You want be sociable? How much you spend? Don't know what she mean. Think she mean party. Everybody holler at me. Doctor tell Turkey turn hose on me. This one hell country, Marchbanks.

How, again,

Osceola Thunderbelly
(Chief of the Crokinoles).

*

MEDITATIONS AT RANDOM

REPULSIVE LITTLE STRANGER / While hanging about a friend's house I picked up a book called *The Culture of the Abdomen*. It proved to be a gloomy work, holding out little hope for the future of Western Civilization unless we immediately get our abdomens into a condition resembling that of the Maoris and South Sea Islanders. These people, it appears, do elaborate dances in which no part of them moves but their abdomens. I don't know that I would care to see the National Ballet go over to this technique, but apparently it is wonderful for the tripes. . . . Even a mediocre writer may create one golden phrase, and the author of this book achieved it in the following sentence: "Upon many a death certificate we read the words Heart Failure, but we know that Fat and Gas are the parents of Heart Failure." What a magically repulsive picture this calls up! Fat, the loath-some Slob-Mate, is approached by Gas, the fluttering, elusive, faintly-squealing Spectre-Bride, who whispers, "Honey, there's going to be a Little Stranger soon – little H.F., that we've always dreamed of!" And then – BANG!

SANCTA SIMPLICITAS / After a longuish chat with some children today, I reflected that the child's attitude toward humour differs sharply from that of the adult. In the world of mature people a joke is funny once, and should never be repeated in the same company. But children, having decided that a joke is funny, go on repeating it, laughing more loudly each time, until they collapse in hysteria. The mental age of a man might be gauged by observing how often he can laugh at the same joke.

KING OF THE BEASTS AT LUNCH / To an excellent film about Africa, with some of the best pictures of wild animals that I have ever seen. I was particularly interested in close-ups of a group of lions eating a zebra. Now I was brought up on picture books which insisted that the lion was a noble beast, that killed its prey with a single violent blow, and then stood upon the fallen carcass for a time, roaring; when it had thus worked up an appetite it tore off a leg, devoured it in lonely splendour and rushed off for further spectacular mischief. But here was a picture of five or six lions, all pushing and shoving like human beings, gobbling the guts of the zebra; there was no roaring, no defiance and no loneliness. One lion lay on its side near the feast, gorged and apparently slightly drunk. Vultures stood nearby, like waiters hoping to clear away the dirty plates. The lions ate messily, dropping bits and slobbering on their fronts. It seems that life in the jungle is rather more like life at a short-order lunch wagon than I had supposed. I do not know whether to be pleased or not.

*

FROM MY FILES

To Haubergeon Hydra, esq.

Dear Mr. Hydra:

I thought that you might like to know that I don't believe the Old Age Pension should be increased. Old age is too delightful and dangerous a state to require a pension. Old people are usually very happy, and they are also subversive and a Bad Example. Let me tell you what I know.

Last Saturday I went to a nearby school for boys to watch their annual cadet inspection. I well remember when I was a schoolboy what an agony these affairs were. For weeks beforehand we marched till our legs were stiff; a sergeant-major with an immense stomach rudely urged us to suck in our non-existent stomachs; we polished our buttons till all the brass was worn off them; we polished our boots inside and out; we learned to march slowly, quickly and imperceptibly; we learned to perform complex quadrilles when other boys shouted hoarse and incomprehensible words. And when The Day came, in an agony of fear we performed these feats, believing that we had the admiration and enthralled attention of our elders. We didn't know whether they admired us or not; our collars were so tight that we were bereft of the senses of sight and hearing. But we believed that they did.

Last Saturday I found out what really went on among the onlookers. While the boys marched, yelled, stamped and drove themselves toward hysterics their elders jabbered among themselves, laughed, averted their eyes from the sweating heroes and occasionally said "Aren't the little boys sweet?" Some of those boys, Mr. Hydra, were daily shavers and not in the least sweet. And who were the worst offenders in this respect? Who mumbled trivialities during the General Salute? Who turned their backs and sniggered at private jokes while The Colours were being marched past? The Old, Mr. Hydra. The happy, carefree, irreverent, unpatriotic Old.

Don't raise their pensions until they smarten up, and show a suitable respect for the Young.

Yours from the philosophical eminences of Middle Life,
        Samuel Marchbanks.

*

To Mr. Adam Mulligrub.

Dear Mulligrub:
    Please send me at once –

(1) 12 bundles containing twelve different Canadian leaves.
(2) 12 packages containing twelve different Canadian nuts.

Some schoolchildren in whom I am interested have been told by their teachers that they must make collections of leaves and nuts as specified above and it occurs to me that you, as a market gardener, are the man to supply them. I shall sell the collections to the children for 50 cents each, or $1.00 for both leaves and nuts, and will send you half. The teacher will be happy, you will be happy, and I shall be happy.

I do not know why the teacher wants this rubbish. The ways of teachers are past understanding. But she wants them, and I have been utterly unsuccessful in getting any together. The fact is, I can only recognize three kinds of leaf. There is the evergreen leaf, which is easy to recognize because it smells like bath salts and probably pricks you. Then there is the maple leaf, which has a jagged edge. All other leaves, to me, are beech leaves.

The teacher thinks differently. She sent one of my small clients back to me with a beech leaf which she said was from a Kentucky coffee tree. Did you ever hear of such a thing? Two other beech leaves she identified as cucumber tree and black cherry. She also asserts that there are 36 kinds of maple and even 6 kinds of willow, which I had always considered a straightforward, honest, one-type tree. The children who bother me about this talk wildly of the mockernut and hickory. I do not believe that such trees exist.

As for nuts, I believed until last week that nuts were made

in those shops which smell so strongly of hot fat. To me a nut has always been a confection, something like a humbug or a Scotch mint. But it appears that nuts grow on trees.

Rush the collections as fast as you can, and I will see if I can drum up any more trade among the Nature Study set. They may be wanting stuffed birds next.

Yours faithfully,

S. Marchbanks.

*

To Raymond Cataplasm, M.D., F.R.C.P.

Dear Dr. Cataplasm:

A physician who writes for the papers says that a slow heartbeat is a good thing. This is just what I have been saying for years, but nobody will listen. You doctors are really the most self-sufficient tribe!

What animals live longest? Those with the slowest heartbeat. I have no figures handy, but I remember hunting them up once in a medical book. An elephant lives to a great age, and its heart beats about 45 times a minute. A tortoise, if my memory serves me aright, has a heartbeat of approximately 22 thumps a minute. When you get down to really long-lived animals, like crocodiles, the beat is likely to be two or three times a minute. And I once pressed my ear to a parrot's bosom (getting badly scratched for my pains) and I couldn't hear any heartbeat at all.

Don't you think you could extend your patients' lives indefinitely, and make your fortune and ruin the insurance companies, simply by giving your patients some simple drug to slow down their hearts to the speed of a crocodile's?

Your perennial patient,

Samuel Marchbanks.

*

To Samuel Marchbanks, ESQ.

Dear Marchbanks:

I can't go on like this! It half-kills me to live near a man who hates me the way you do! My lawyers say that if you take that case to court it might cost me my shirt, even if I win. I'm sorry I put the skunk in your car. Honest, Marchbanks!

So here's what I'll do. I'll sell you my car, at a sacrifice. It is a Pierce Arrow 1923, and I'll let you have it for $1,500, cash.

I can't say fairer than that, can I?

Your despondent neighbour,

Dick Dandiprat.

*

To Richard Dandiprat, ESQ.

Abhorred Dandiprat:

The jaws of our irresistible legal system are closing upon you. It will be my pleasure, when the jaws open, to pick you out of their teeth.

Yours with demoniacal laughter,
Marchbanks.

*

COMMUNIQUÉ (*written on brown paper previously used for wrapping meat*)

To Big Chief Marchbanks.

How, Marchbanks!

You been in West, Marchbanks. I once in West. Went with harvest excursion but not like work so get job carving totem poles for Haida tribe. Haida sell poles to tourists, but can't carve fast enough so start production line. My job always carve big Thunder Bird on top of pole. You know Thunder Bird, Marchbanks. Fierce face with big nose, like magistrate. I carve Thunder Bird to look like every magistrate ever put me in jail. Good fun. But awful hard work, so every day I take 4 quart pail of beer to totem pole factory so I can rest my mind once in a while. One day big fat woman tourist come to factory. You Haida Indian, she say. No me Crokinole Indian, I say. Then you are impostor, she say. No, that kind of printer, I say. What you make there, she say. That Thunder Bird, I say. What that tin pail, she say. That Thunder Mug for Thunder Bird, I say. Joke, Marchbanks. Always joke with squaw. But she screech and tell her friends I am bad man and talk dirty to her. Lie, Marchbanks. Her man friend get cross with me. Why you talk dirty to my wife, he say. She lie to make herself important, I say; I only talk dirty to pretty squaw. He get mad and make big noise and fat woman screech. When they go away I resign from Thunder Bird job. Artist got delicate nerves, Marchbanks. Can't stand uproar. You buy any totem poles, Marchbanks? You got money? I need money

How, again,
Osceola Thunderbelly,
Chief of the Crokinoles.

*

To Mr. Adam Mulligrub, Landscape Architect.

Dear Mulligrub:

You ask what kind of hedging I want along the southern boundary of the pleasure grounds at Marchbanks Towers. As a matter of fact I have a special problem there, of which I should have told you. It is at that point that my neighbour, Richard Dandiprat, invades my property in order to take my wheel barrow or my hose, or to recover the ball which he childishly bounces against the side of his house, or to make a shortcut to the bus stop. I have considered various types of thorn bushes but none of them, I fear, would quite fill the need.

Therefore I want you to fill a somewhat unusual order. Will you send to Central Africa for forty small Upas trees, and plant them in hedge formation at the necessary point. The Upas, with which you may not be familiar, is a tree which possesses long tentacles, like those of an octopus; at the end of each tentacle is a sucker of exceptional strength; when any living thing comes within reach of the Upas tree it grabs it with its suckers and drags it to the centre of the tree, where it tears off the flesh, and throws the bones upon the ground; it is upon flesh obtained in this way that the tree is nourished. A good planting of Upas will give me just the hedge I need, I think, and if Dandiprat and any of the neighbourhood dogs disappear it will be a good lesson to trespassers.

Warn the Customs men to be careful when examining the plants, will you? I don't want any trouble with the Government, which would probably expect me to pay for the uniforms of any missing officials.

Yours faithfully,
S. Marchbanks.

＊

LES PENSÉES DE MARCHBANKS

BABIES AND THE ADULT MALE / Across the street from my work-room window is an apartment which has a bay-window at my level; during the past few weeks a baby has been making regular appearances there, so that the doings in the street below may entertain it. I judge that it is a male baby, and it is a fine, large child, with a solemn and philosophical countenance. The baby views the street and I view the baby. I like babies, under special circumstances, and by a lucky chance the relationship between me and this particular baby perfectly fulfils all my conditions.

I can see it, but I cannot hear it; I can admire its winning ways, and laugh indulgently when it topples over, but it is not near enough to wet me; when it wants anything, a pair of hands appear from behind it with the desired object. This is ideal, and I am thinking of putting this baby in my will. I believe that if the truth were known, my attitude toward this baby is that of most adult males; men like children, but they do not like them to be too close. Some barrier – as for instance a wide street, filled with traffic – between a man and a baby, acts as a powerful stimulant to affection between them.

THE MAGIC OF LATIN / Among the tools of my trade I possess a number of books of quotations, most of which bear titles such as *Familiar Quotations*, *Quotations The Whole World Loves*, and the like. The only honestly named one is *The Oxford Dictionary of Quotations*. The fact is that no great fat thick book of quotations can be called "familiar"; very few people can identify more than a dozen of them. Furthermore there are hundreds of quotations in such books which I solemnly swear are not familiar to anybody. The fake profundities of dead politicians, the treacly outpourings of fifth-rate poets, the moonlit nonsense of minor essayists – this junk makes up the bulk of most quotation books. I like Mencken's book of quotations because it is full of sin and impudence and does not pretend to be familiar; I like the Oxford book because it is unashamedly highbrow and contains a great many quotations in Latin. But the "familiar" nonsense I scorn. I love Latin quotations. I suspect that nobody ever said anything in Latin which was above the level of barber shop philosophy, but it has a wondrous sonority.

LASS WITH THE DELICATE AIR / In a periodical I found a picture of a lovely girl in evening dress; she was able to keep up the social pace, the advertisement said, because she took two indigestion pellets after each meal. Now this is melancholy reading, if you like! I do not choose to think of beautiful girls as eating at all, much less digesting. And the notion that a beautiful girl stuffs herself with dyspepsia tablets all the time is utterly repugnant to me. As an amateur of physiology I know that every human creature has enough acid in its gizzard to eat a hole in a heavy steel beam; as a romantic admirer of Womanhood I decline to apply my knowledge to the young and fair. A girl with indigestion is a traitor to her sex and, much worse, a traitor to mine.

*

To Samuel Marchbanks, ESQ.

Dear Mr. Marchbanks:

I write to enlist your support and membership in the Canadian Laudable Litter League which I am forming. Do you realize, sir, that every day thousands of pounds – nay, tons – of material of one sort and another which should be returned to the soil of our country is burned, or washed down our waterways to the sea, never to be recovered? Vital vitamins, irreplaceable minerals and animal and vegetable matter of all kinds is wasted in this way. The time has come to Call a Halt.

During the Summer I have been doing my bit to preserve what is Canada's for Canada. Whenever I have been on a picnic I have taken care to throw my hard-boiled eggshell back on the land, to preserve minerals. I have thrown my banana skins and other peelings into farmers' fields, to put vitamins back into the soil. When others have gathered up their waste paper, I have left it to blow where the wind listeth, for it came from the soil and should return whence it came.

Each member of the Laudable Litter League pledges himself never again to give his garbage to a wasteful urban collector, for burning; instead he takes it into the country (preferably in the dark of the moon, as this is the time approved by our hero, the late Rudolf Steiner) and throws it into the field of some farmer whose soil appears to be impoverished. This should be done by stealth, for the League seeks no credit for its good work.

Begging you to become an honorary L.L.D. (Laudable Litter Distributor) at once, I remain,

Yours literally,
Minerva Hawser.

*

To Haubergeon Hydra, ESQ.

Dear Mr. Hydra:

As I have written to you so often in tones of complaint, it gives me particular pleasure to pay you a compliment on the agreeable manners of the men who deal with immigration on the international bridges at Niagara Falls. As Overseer of Conduct for Civil Servants I thought that you would like to hear about this. During the past month I had some work to do in Niagara Falls, Canada, but I was living with some friends in Niagara Falls, USA, and I use the bridges a good deal.

Each time I crossed I answered much the same questions. "Where were you born?" "Skunk's Misery, Ontario," I would reply, in an accent which I acquired abroad, and which has at various times caused me to be taken for an Englishman, an Iris‌man, a Scotsman, and a native of the Scilly Isles. This accent, an‌ an appearance which suggests an archimandrite of the Greek Orthodox Church, sometimes throws doubt on my Skunk's Misery origin. But I was always believed. Then, after a few more queries about my sex life and financial status, I would be passed through, with bows and cries of "Huzza for Marchbanks!" If I had any luggage the Customs men would finger it delicately, compliment me on the neatness of my packing and the exquisite taste which I showed in choosing socks and underpants, and wave me on.

The bridge attendants have a sterner side, however, as I saw on my last journey across the bridge. The man who came after me was elderly, with flowing white hair and a goatee – obviously a Southern Colonel. "Have you anything to declare?" asked the Canadian Immigration man. "I declare it's a mighty hot day, suh!" said the Colonel. As I drove away he was dragged into the Customs House and the thud of cudgels on pulpy flesh mingled with screams in a Southern accent rent the air. Presumably he was suspected of importing a joke, which would of course have been intolerable to our local funnymen, completely upsetting the economy of their trade.

Yours loyally,
Samuel Marchbanks.

*

To Chandos Fribble, ESQ.

Esteemed Fribble:

I want you to look into a curious psychological twist which has recently become observable in advertisements for cars. One of these (I need not specify the maker's name) shows a young man who is about to kiss a very pretty girl, but turns his head at the vital moment to look at a passing car. The second shows a young man in the act of telling a charming girl that he loves her hair, her eyes, and her father's new car. The third shows a young couple doting upon – a baby? each other? – no, upon a bright shiny car.

Now, Fribble, it looks to me as though the North American male were beginning to exalt motor cars to the position in his esteem once held by women. This is dangerous, and I would like to find out how far it has gone. For if this trend continues the day is not far off when the American male will mate, not with a woman, but with his car, and the result of this union will probably be a winsome, cuddly little motorcycle.

Yours in alarm,
Samuel Marchbanks.

Waghorn Wittol, ESQ.

ear Wittol:

I understand your position exactly. When strange men call on the phone and want to know where Mrs. Wittol is, or to describe to you their feelings toward Mrs. Wittol, it must be very boring for you. But why do you not develop a technique for such callers?

For years I have used a variety of methods for discouraging phoners who are nuisances. The simplest, and one of the best, is to pretend that you can't hear, and demand repetitions, which you interrupt with cries of "It's no use: I can't hear a word you say." But it is also a good idea to lay the phone down gently, and then to go elsewhere and read a book. This gives the impression that you have been carried off by fairies, or perhaps a great eagle. Sneezing and coughing into the instrument are also effective, when followed by a muttered "Excuse me," and another blast, or perhaps a groan. And you can always pretend to be talking to someone else in the room with you, so that the phoner gets an impression of divided attention.

There are dozens of ways to discourage telephoners. You must learn to protect yourself. Regards to your wife – if she is still yours.

Marchbanks.

*

FROM MY MEDITATIONS

MUSICAL PUZZLER / Mingled with some musical people today, almost on terms of equality. I like musical people but I am always astonished by the dogmatic quality of their statements, especially when they are young. For instance, a young lady who was probably about nineteen asserted this afternoon that J. S. Bach had embraced the whole scope of human feelings in his music in a manner more sublime than that of any other composer. I could not permit this to pass. "Where does Bach make even a passable stab at an expression of romantic love?" I asked her, and she could not answer. And truly old Bach, who had two wives and twenty children, had not much to say about this important matter; the majesty of his harmony and the remorseless deedle-doodle of his counterpoint were not geared for it, and in this sphere such lesser creatures as Puccini beat him hollow. The young woman took her revenge by behaving toward me as if I had no soul, which was typically feminine, and pained me not at all. I have quite a large soul – a number 9.

SCENTING AN AUDIENCE / In a weak moment some months ago I agreed to talk to a women's club today. I am a hardy optimist; when people ask me to make speeches several months before the appointed time I often accept, stupidly thinking that in the interval something will happen to prevent me from making good my promise. But the fateful day always comes, and there I am, on my feet, clutching my notes, with despair in my heart. An audience entirely of men is bad enough, but an audience entirely of women is as frightening as a battery of machine guns. There is one thing about female audiences, though – they have a delicious smell. Powder, expensive textiles and scent – all favourite sniffs of mine, – combine to make them more glorious than a June garden. I am sure not one of these ladies today was wearing any scent below the rank of Chanel Number Five, and I thought I detected several twenty-five-dollars-an-ounce whiffs, for they were wealthy women, knee-deep in good works. So I inhaled deeply and gave tongue. Audiences of men smell of cigars, whisky, and shoe-polish, which inspires me with solemn and world-shaking thoughts, unsuitable for the more delicate intellects of women.

UNVEILING THE FEET / A rainy day, and this afternoon I attended a gathering at which several ladies appeared in overshoes of a type new to me. They were not the honest old goloshes which for generations have made Canadian women look like Brahma hens, but new-fangled creations of a milky-semi-transparent plastic, which gave their feet a mysterious air and which, when removed, looked like the ghosts of overshoes. Several ladies, I also observed, wore what appeared to be bedsocks under their goloshes, but upon closer examination I found that these were little bags which they wore to protect their shoes from being scratched by the (presumably) harshly abrasive linings of their overshoes. There is no enchantment in the spectacle of a woman unwrapping her feet; in my younger days girls wore heavy knitted bloomers over their fine silk-step-ins when attending winter parties, but they always took them off in a room provided for that purpose. A room for foot-unveiling would save much coy balancing in hallways.

DECLINING ART / Pondered upon the decline of the once great art of Striking-the-Match-on-the-Seat of the Pants; I saw a girl in slacks trying to do so, and although she had an impressive acreage of taut trouser upon which to work she could not manage it. A girl! The greatest master of this art I ever knew was an employee in a woodyard, who never spoke of girls save in terms of obscene contempt; how his oaken heart would ache, and his teak head tremble, if he knew that now only girls seek to excel in the trick of which he was a master. He relit his pipe – a short clay – at least fifty times every morning, and always struck his match with a glorious ripping sound upon his blue-jeaned fundament. He died when a load of logs fell on him; if he had survived, shame would finish him now.

CROWNING ENORMITY / I can no longer deceive myself that Autumn is not here, so today I retrieved my hat from the bottom of the hall cupboard, where somebody had stood an umbrella in it, and put it on. This Assumption of the Hat is a symbolic act with me, marking the end of Summer. As I trudged to work I saw many men wearing hats which bore unmistakable signs of imprisonment in hall cupboards; there is a crippled look about the brim of a long-disused hat which is ignominious. The wearers, too, have a self-conscious look, as though they expected people to laugh at them. In the 'Twenties the enthusiasm for going without a hat in Summer arose, simultaneously with the Decline of the Straw Boater. It was thought to be good for the hair to expose it to the sun, wind, soot, sand, smog, fall-out and other elements. Even bald men allowed the Sun to beat down upon their poor skulls, hoping that some sort of vegetation might be encouraged thereby. The delusion that going without a hat is good for the hair has long since been abandoned; ordinary common sense shows that it is bad for the hair, making it dirty, dry and frizzled. But the habit persists, and every year, come Michaelmas, we have to learn to wear hats all over again.

*

COMMUNIQUÉ (*discovered in entrails of a wild duck, written on birchbark*)

To Big Chief Marchbanks.

How, Marchbanks:
    This one hell country, Marchbanks. Look at weather. Every Fall people say to me how about Winter. And I say long Winter or short Winter if bears go to sleep or sit up till maybe Christmas. This year my best bear that I trust nearly twenty year go to sleep awful early. He sound asleep right after hunting season. So I say to everybody long hard Winter cause bear asleep. But no hard Winter come. So I go to bear nest and look inside. Bear sound asleep. What hell, I think. Then I see bottle in bear paw.

Grab bottle. It say sleeping pills on outside, Marchbanks. Bear steal bottle from some big city hunter, busy fellow can't sleep without pills. Bear eat every pill. Bear sleep like dead. I wish big city hunter stay out of woods. They ruin woods and weather forecast business for good Indian.

How again,
> Osceola Thunderbelly,
> Chief of the Crokinoles.

*

CULLED FROM THE APOPHTHEGMS OF WIZARD MARCHBANKS

It is hard to make an empty bag stand upright; even the most complete Social Security scheme can scarcely achieve it.

Scorpio

♏

the children of this sign are bitter & inveterate enemies, but v. faithful to their lovers & friends.

♀ Mars

A fixed, watery sign

Hesiah Scissorbill & Oct. 51, ...
Halloween & v. appropriate.

(October 24 to November 22)

SCORPIO IS the sign of the Scorpion, and those born under its influence are especially gifted in all matters relating to sex. It is usual for works on astrology to advise the Scorpio-born to do all that they can to master and subdue this remarkable and, let it be said, uncommon advantage. Wizard Marchbanks takes no such unrealistic attitude. You will find that most people are doubtful of their capacities in this respect; it is here that you have the advantage of them, and you would be stupid not to use it, for it is virtually the only advantage you have in the battle of life. You can do with a glance what others must toil to achieve and in the arts of entertainment you are invaluable, though rarely talented. Do not attempt to rival those born under other signs in such accomplishments as conversation or elegant attire, but concentrate on your specialty and in the end everything and virtually everybody will fall into your lap.

Enchantment-of-the-Month

>*⤳⊛⤳*⤳⊛⤳*⤳⊛⤳*⤳⊛⤳*⤳⊛

Not a bad group of colours for you: gold, yellow, red and orange.
Your flowers are the honeysuckle and red carnation. Your gems,
the moon crystal and the topaz. All astrological authorities, from
the earliest to those appearing last year, are agreed that Scorpio
people are very lucky in love – and when they say love, they do not
mean mooning on a swing-seat on a verandah, but real-blood-
and-thunder stuff with Eternal Triangles, Wagnerian music and
pistols-for-two-and-coffee-for-one. Understandably, with a fate
like this, you will need a fairly extensive wardrobe of gold,
yellow and red clothes, and if you are a man you will naturally
have a standing order for red carnation buttonholes with a
reliable florist. Persons born under other signs are warned to be
particularly careful of emotional entanglements with those born
under Scorpio. A nod is as good as a wink to a blind horse: a nod
or a wink to the Scorpio-born may mean the end of your peace
of mind for quite a long time.

Health Hints for Those Born Under Scorpio

I do not intend to discuss your special focus of physical weakness
with you. All I say is Look Out! Wizard Marchbanks flatly
declines to discuss this matter further, and will *not*, however
opulent the bribe, send any additional information in a plain,
self-addressed envelope.

*

REFLECTIONS

STEALTHY TERROR / There is an ugly development in the cellars
at the Towers. I discovered a few days ago that a jar of brandied
peaches which I had prepared against the Christmas festival
had popped its seal, and made a mental note to do something
about it. Today, when I got around to this chore, I found that a
third of the peaches and a third of the brandy were gone, and
there were signs about that mice were the culprits. Does this
mean that a coven of inebriated mice are at large somewhere in
my house, engaged in who can say what excesses? A mouse with
a brandy jag might turn ugly, and decide that it wanted my bed.
I am not unnerved by mice, as some people are, but they tickle,
and what is more, their personal hygiene is of the most elementary sort. A mouse is not the lovable little creature that Disney
presented to the world; it is as much like a rat as a pony is like
a horse, and its disposition is unstable. I am rather worried about
129 *

this situation, for I do not know how many mice have been at the brandy; ten or more could easily take over the proprietorship of the Towers, in a sudden, mutinous rush. I sat all evening with ears cocked, listening for tiny hiccups, almost too high for the human ear to detect, behind the wainscot.

A VULGAR ERROR / A man said to me today that what ailed the modern world was that it had forgotten about the Seven Deadly Sins. Not to be outdone in this line of argument I said that I considered that it was far worse that we had forgotten the Four Cardinal Virtues. He goggled, and had plainly never heard of these, so I named them – Prudence, Temperance, Justice and Fortitude. He was himself an exemplar of what ails the world, with his yelping about sin, and his neglect of virtue. I suppose the poor boob thought that mere abstention from sin was virtue enough – a common, comical and somewhat criminal error.

MEALINESS OF MOUTH / "What pretty china!" exclaimed a guest who was taking a dish of tea at Marchbanks Towers this afternoon. "Madam," said I, in what I hope was a polite tone, "that is not china, but crockery, and if you don't know the difference between the two it is time you found out." . . . The North American continent is afflicted with a vast amount of pseudo-gentility; we hate to call things by their proper names, and as a result we degrade and debase a number of fine words. Any fool knows china when he sees it; it is porcelain, has an unmistakable glow and finish, and can be wrought much thinner than crockery; crockery – which includes most of the vessels from which we eat and drink – is thicker, and in spite of its glaze it has no glow. It is made of clay, and looks it. There is no shame in using crockery; it is good, honest stuff and some of it has great beauty. But why pretend that it is china? If you can judge the height of the tea through the side of the cup, you are drinking from china; if you can't, you aren't. . . . It is this same mealy-mouthed prissiness which describes any old chunk of cloudy bottle-glass as "crystal."

WISDOM OF GILBERT / Saw the D'Oyly Carte opera company perform *H.M.S. Pinafore*, which I first saw them do when I was twelve and which I have seen roughly ten times since. Pondered upon this piece and the Gilbert and Sullivan operas in general. Though not a fanatic I am fond of them, not only because they are true works of art in themselves but because of the orderly, reasonable, intelligent and literate Victorian world of which they are a distorted reflection. There is a background of good sense and real wit to Gilbert's libretti; this afternoon, at a tenth view, I saw more clearly than before what a wry and pungent piece of work *Pinafore* is; like *Gulliver's Travels* you may take it as a pleasant phantasy, or as a powerful kick in the slats to all stratified societies, including those of the North American continent and the USSR. The Gilbert and Sullivan operas have been extravagantly praised for many reasons, but never, to my knowledge, for the savage and often melancholy wisdom that is in them; Sir William Gilbert was not a nice man, and his operas are not nice. They are something rarer; they are wise.

*

FROM MY FILES

To Haubergeon Hydra, ESQ.

Dear Mr. Hydra:

I have been asked by several influential members of the Canadian Brotherhood of Snow Shovellers and Ploughmen to put their case to you as Pro. Tem. Sub-Re-Router of Labour, in order that you may draw it to the attention of the appropriate Minister. Here is our case in a nutshell:

(a) Some winters it snows a lot and we make money.
(b) Other winters it doesn't snow much and we don't make any money.
(c) We want a floor under snow. That is, in winter when the crop of snow is poor, we want the Government either to distribute false snow – salt, flour, Western wheat or something of that sort – so that we can shovel it and make money, OR –
(d) We want the Government to pay us for shovelling snow that isn't there, so we can make money.

You will see at once that this is in the latest economic trend and a good idea. See what you can do for us, like a good fellow, and some Christmas Santa may have something in his sack for a good Civil Servant.

Love and kisses from all us snowmen,
Samuel Marchbanks.

*

To Samuel Marchbanks, ESQ.

My Dear Nephew:

Earlier this Summer your Uncle Gomeril and I observed our seventy-fifth wedding anniversary. You did not send a greeting card, for which abstention I thank you; we received several cards, all of a nauseating degree of sentimentality, bearing no conceivable relationship to the sort of domesticity your Uncle and I have waged during the past three-quarters of a century. You might, however, have sent a few flowers. Several people sent bouquets of what I learned as a girl to call "wind-flowers," but what people now call "everlastings." Whether this was intended as a delicate reference to the unusual durability of our match, or whether it was an ironical allusion to the hardy good health which we both enjoy I cannot determine.

We celebrated the occasion by visiting Niagara Falls for a few days, to rest and observe the great Natural Wonder. The Chamber of Commerce there offers a certificate of congratulation to all honeymoon couples, upon which appears a wish that their union may be as beautiful and enduring as the Falls itself. It occurred to me that the Falls is as much distinguished for its violence and its extreme dampness as for beauty and endurance, but as your Uncle and I completed our honeymoon and all that goes with it long ago this was a matter of merely academic concern to us.

We were, however, much affronted by the number of honeymooners who infested the place, wandering about hand in hand, wet smiles and goggling eyes proclaiming their condition for all the world to see. When your Uncle and I were married and went to the Shetlands on our wedding trip we took great pains to look like a married couple of several years standing.

Perhaps we were foolish so to do, but I think that our reticence was preferable to the mawkish displays of unfledged connubiality which we observed at N.F.

We visited, among other places, a restaurant maintained by the Provincial Government, at which a bottle of wine cost almost twice as much as it does in a liquor store, also maintained by the Provincial Government. Your Uncle commented upon this in his accustomed ringing tones, but of what avail is it to protest against official extortion? Complaining about a government is, as Holy Writ tersely phrases it, kicking against the pricks.

Your affectionate aunt-by-marriage,
Bathsheba Marchbanks.

*

To Genghis Marchbanks, ESQ.

Dear Cousin Genghis:

I am terribly sorry that I was unable to be present at the Gala Opening of your new pawnshop. I understand that it was a wonderful affair, and distinguished by your own special brand of hospitality. Water ran like water, I am told, and guests who had brought their own sandwiches were permitted to eat them on the premises.

Let me deal with your last letter, before bringing up anything else. No, I do not want any binoculars at specially reduced prices, nor am I in the market for the telescope which you offer cheap. I have never been able to see nearly as well through binoculars as through my own unassisted eyes. No doubt this is sheer optical obstinacy, but it is true. And I have never been able to see anything at all through a telescope.

This is not for lack of goodwill. I admire telescopes, and would love to clap one to my eye, sailor-fashion, while taking a walk in the country, or even when attending the ballet. But all a telescope does for me is to flatten my eyewinkers uncomfortably.

But I am in the market for a good concertina. Concertinas run in the Marchbanks family. Uncle Fortunatus plays one. I play one. And the other day I discovered our little niece Imoinda extracting the usual cow-stuck-in-a-swamp noises from a concertina which I discarded some years ago when I bought my super-Wheatstone. Can you find a nice instrument for Imoinda which some needy concertinist has hocked?

Your affectionate cousin,
Sam.

*

To Miss Nancy Frisgig.

Charming Nancy:

I have been neglecting you shamefully; almost as shamefully as you have been neglecting me. But I write now to tell you of a discovery I have made which should be of interest to the whole female sex, and particularly to that part of it which, like yourself, is chiefly concerned with matters of fashion and allurement.

What is the greatest single beautifier available to womanhood? Is it a cream, or a top-dressing for the face, or a perfume which steals away the critical judgement of the beholder? No, poppet, it is shoes that fit.

How did I find this out? Well, yesterday I sat in a restaurant, munching a bowl of breakfast food – it was evening, but I practically live on breakfast food – when in came a young man with, obviously, his Best Girl. She was stylishly dressed; her hair was nicely arranged, and she wore a few gew-gaws which indicated that she came from a home of some wealth and possibly even of cultivation. But her face was the mask of a Gorgon.

They sat down near me, and immediately, under the table, I saw her kick off her shoes. And at once her face melted into that expression – half Madonna, half Aphrodite – which reduces the male to a jelly. Beauty suffused her as though the moon had sailed from behind a cloud. She ordered a steak at $6.50, and a peck of lobster and a Baked Alaska to go with it, and her escort did not even notice. It was worth it, he seemed to think, to be the companion of that girl.

Now, Nancy, if that girl means to make the most of her considerable gifts, she must either go barefoot, or get the shoes she needs. And so I say to all her sex.

Yours with warmest admiration down to the ankles,
  Sam.

*

To Samuel Marchbanks, ESQ.

Dear Cousin:

I have your letter, and as someone left half a sheet of paper in the pawnshop yesterday when they were pledging their diamonds, I take my pen in hand at once to reply. You should not speak so lightly of the concertina, Cousin. Are you not aware that there is quite a little body of music composed especially for it? Tschaikowsky arranged his second orchestral suite so that it might be played on four concertinas. Molique wrote a concerto for the concertina, as well as a sonata for concertina and piano. Regondi, too, wrote a concerto for the instrument. Did you not know that the late Arthur Balfour was a most accomplished player, and a concertina was the solace of his idle hours during his time in Parliament? I shall get one for little Imoinda, of course, but I entreat you to see that the child realizes that she handles a sensitive instrument, and not a toy.

Your reproachful kinsman,
  Genghis Marchbanks.

*

To Amyas Pilgarlic, ESQ.

Dear Pil:

I was reading an interesting book the other day about the worship of the Bull-god, Minos, in early Crete. It appears that the High Priest had a golden head, like that of a bull, which he wore over his own head when greeting visitors. He then removed it, and carried on conversation face to face. When he thought that the interview had gone on long enough or that he wanted his visitor to go, he put the bull's head back on again, in sign that the talk was over.

Don't you think that something of this kind could be worked out for people like myself, who never know how to bring an interview to a close? I don't suppose a gold bull's head would really do. It might seem a little eccentric and ostentatious. But a simple brass head, made in the shape of my own face, but stern and impassive, might be just the thing. Or, on second thoughts, better make it bronze. Brass has such a nasty smell, as anyone can learn by sniffing the bell of an old bugle.

There are for sale in joke shops rubber masks, which give one the appearance of a gorilla. I think I shall get one and try it out. If it works I shall get a bronze job done. Do you know of any good cheap foundry which would undertake such a commission?

Yours faithfully,
Sam.

*

To Mervyn Noseigh, M.A.

Dear Mr. Noseigh:

When you put the question to me so baldly – "What led you to become a writer?" – I am momentarily nonplussed. On what level do you expect me to answer? The objective? If so, I became a writer because it looked like easy money. But that won't look well in your PH.D. thesis, so let us try the subjective approach.

On this level, I became a writer because I suffered the early conditioning of the Unconscious that makes writers. That is to say, my Oedipus Complex was further complicated by the *Warmefläsche-reaktion*.

You know how this works. Think of the Infantile World as a Huge Bed; on one side lies Mum, on the other side lies Dad, and in the middle is Baby Bunting. The normal thing, of course, is for B.B. to work out his Oedipus Complex; he wants to kill Dad and mate with Mum – thereby fitting himself for some normal occupation like the Civil Service. But sometimes B.B., *for reasons still unknown to science*, turns from Mum and snuggles up to Dad who quite understandably shoves B.B. down to the bottom of the bed and warms his feet on him as if he were a hot-water bottle (or (*Warmefläsche*). Thus, in the very dawn of his existence, B.B. acquires that down-trodden cast of mind that marks the writer.

Very often Dad kicks B.B. right out of bed onto the cold linoleum, bringing about that sense of Utter Rejection which turns B.B. into a critic.

I can hardly wait to read your thesis.

Reverently,
Samuel Marchbanks (your *topic*).

THE UNIVERSAL FRIEND / As I stood on Yonge Street this afternoon, a man approached me with a happy smile. He stopped in front of me, rocked on his heels, puffed out a cloud of boozy breath and said, "Well, well, well!" As I am peculiarly attractive to persons in his condition, I feigned ignorance of his presence, but he came nearer, and peeped searchingly into my eyes. "Ain't goin' to speak t'an ole pal?" he said, coyly. "How do you do," I said, stiffly. "Cheest," said he "I wouldna thought ole Jock would gimme the brushoff." "You are mistaken, my good fellow," said I. "Gwan," said he; "you're old Jock McGladdeny." "No," said I, firmly. He looked at me, and a gummy tear crept sluggishly down one cheek. "Ole Jock," said he, "an' he won't speak t'an old pal." He took his cigar out of his mouth and prodded me with the wet end of it. "God love yuh, anyway, Jock," he said, and stumbled on, and as he receded I heard him murmur, "Old Jock a Judas; Cheest!" . . . I wonder why I am so often mistaken for somebody else, especially by drunks? Do my features in some mysterious way suggest a Universal Friend – a man whom everybody, at some time or other, has known? This is a cross I bear with very ill grace.

VEXATIOUS VERGE / As winter draws on I sigh with gratitude, for soon one of the problems of Marchbanks Towers will be out of my hands for a few months. I refer to the condition of what I think of as My Verge. Outside my fence is a section of miserable grass which belongs not to me but to the whole community; and the whole community, when passing, throws candy-wrappers, cellophane, cigarette boxes, used paper handkerchiefs, banana skins, dead cats and soiled undergarments upon it, quite casually and without malice. But if I do not occasionally clean up this community trash-heap the Towers begins to look as though it were situated in the middle of a dump. So I stumble brokenly about, with a bag and a nail on the end of a stick, picking up junk, and little children say, "Mummy, shall I give that poor old man a nickel?" when they pass. But with the coming of winter the snow flings its veil of pristine whiteness over my Verge, and conceals the trash, eventually imbedding it in ice. There have been times when I have considered following the example of those citizens of Newfoundland, who have their lawns paved with asphalt, for I notice that few people throw trash on the sidewalks. But I am still a public park-keeper, and will probably continue in my servitude.

DIET SADISM / I have been reading a lot of books about dieting for my physician has spoken prayerfully to me on this subject What annoys me about diet books is that they are written either by people who are funny, or people who are angry. The funny ones think it is the most hilarious thing in the world to be compelled to eat less than one wants, of foods that one would not ordinarily choose; they write as though a diet were a huge joke. The angry ones are worse: they threaten the dieter with quick and unpleasant death if he doesn't lose his excess weight, and they speak scornfully of the kind of life (cocktails and two-helpings-of-everything) which makes diets necessary. Both kinds of writers are crypto-Calvinists who have an addiction to gelatin in food; everything they recommend seems to contain either lettuce or gelatin. Now it so happens that an uncle of mine, Bellerophon Marchbanks, has devoted his life to the manufacture of gelatin and also of glue, and I cannot separate the two in my mind. Gelatin in moderation I accept; unlimited gelatin turns me cold and shaky to begin, and then produces the effect anyone could foresee as proceeding from a diet of glue – anyone but a doctor, that's to say.

THE MEASURED STEP / A few weeks ago I bought myself a toy – a pedometer, which measures how far I walk when I am wearing it. Apparently I don't walk very much. I have always assumed that in the course of an ordinary day's work I walked four or five miles, but according to the pedometer an eighth of a mile is nearer the correct figure. The only time the pedometer gets much of a workout is when I am cutting my lawn, and then the miles tick up at a surprising rate. The instrument is worn on the right leg, and it has a psychological effect; it makes me stamp with that leg to make sure that the dial registers properly, and I am developing a gait like the Giant Blunderbore, or possibly Peg-Leg Pete the Pirate. The Pedometer cheats, too; when I am riding in a car it registers a step whenever the car goes over a bump; on a long journey I can cover as much as a quarter of a mile, according to the pedometer, although I have not exerted myself in the least. I have no desire to clock astonishing scores on this gadget; I merely want to know if I do much walking. I am disappointed by what it tells me, but at least I am now in a position to lure other people to boast of the walking they do in an ordinary day's work, so that I may contradict them, and gain face as a statistician.

*

To Samuel Marchbanks, ESQ.

Dear Sir:

It comes to our ears from a professional source that you are bringing suit against your neighbour, Richard Dandiprat, whom you accuse of imprisoning a skunk (*Mephitis Canadensis*) in your motor car, with resultant damage to same.

We learn also that the success of your suit is jeopardized by your inability to bring forward a single witness who saw Dandiprat commit this misdemeanour.

May we offer our services? For a modest fee we can provide witnesses who will give your case all the corroboration which it needs, ensuring your success. We feel that three capable witnesses (two men and a woman) would amply meet your requirements, and we will provide these for five hundred dollars and expenses. You will agree that this is a ridiculously low sum, and it is only because we work on a very large scale that we are able to make this very special price. All correspondence strictly confidential.

Yours, etc.,

False Witness, Inc.

Telegraphic Address:

"ANANIAS"

*

To Mordecai Mouseman, ESQ.

Dear Mouseman:

I enclose a letter which I have received from a firm which seems to have just what we want. The trial draws near – at least I hope it does, for it is now almost a year since Dandiprat ruined my car – and I will not tolerate any fumbling. I want Dandiprat to get at least two years hard labour. We want witnesses; these people have them. Will you attend to the matter?

Yours,

Samuel Marchbanks.

*

To Samuel Marchbanks, ESQ.

Dear Mr. Marchbanks:

Oh, Mr. Marchbanks, sir! Oh, unhappiest of our clients!! Oh, luckless litigant!!! How often have I not counselled you against taking any step without consulting your lawyer; how often has

* 138

not our senior partner, Mr. Jabez Mouseman (now, alack, pr
upon a bed of pain – shingles, I grieve to say) given you t
same tried and true advice? Tell me – though I dread the answe.
knowing your fiery and impetuous nature – have you given any
money to False Witness, Inc.? For if you have, all is lost indeed!

Understand, my dear sir, that not only do you sully the
whole fabric of British justice by suggesting that we employ
these people; you gravely endanger your case, as well. The
fabric of British justice has been sullied, and dry-cleaned, many
times; like an Oriental rug, it shows only the very largest stains;
but there is not a judge on the bench in this country who does
not know every employee of False Witness, Inc., intimately. For
years they have paraded in and out of the witness boxes of
Canada dropping the wigs, false whiskers, wooden legs and
other unconvincing paraphernalia with which they seek to
disguise themselves, and their appearance is now a signal for
derisive laughter in every court in the land.

False Witness, Inc. employs all the Canadian actors who
are so bad that they cannot even get jobs with CBC-TV. Far better
no witness than a False Witness.

I am shocked, sir, that you should think a firm such as ours
would lend itself to underhand practice. We rely entirely upon
the probity of the court, and the forensic brilliance of our bar-
rister, Mr. Cicero Forcemeat. You will understand the unique
distinction attaching to Mr. Forcemeat when I tell you that he is
one of the half-dozen lawyers in the country who is not a Q.C.

And if we feel that the support of expert testimony is
required, we know where to get it without resort to the broken-
down dialect comedians who work for False Witness, Inc.

Yours chidingly,
    Mordecai Mouseman
    (for Mouseman, Mouseman and Forcemeat).

*

PENSÉES DE MARCHBANKS

CAUSE AND EFFECT / The wonders of science will never cease to
stagger me. A friend of mine possesses a large powerful dog, so
that I rarely go to his house, but today I met him on the street.
He told me that he was well, "And Schneider is completely
himself again, too," he added. (Schneider is the dog.) I enquired
politely what had ailed Schneider, though in my inmost heart I
cared little. "Poor fellow went all to pieces a few weeks ago,"
said my friend; "completely forgot his house-training. It was
terrible. He knew it was wrong, and he looked ashamed – you

what an expressive face Schneider has – but didn't seem to able to help himself. With a big dog, you know, that's serious. the wife began to resent Schneider. Said either one or other of them would have to go. Tried to get Schneider to wear diapers, but other dogs laughed at him. So I took him to the vet. Vet said, 'That's easy,' and washed some big lumps of wax out of Schneider's ears. 'Now he'll be all right,' said the vet, and sure enough, he is. House-broken as a lamb. Schneider happy; wife happy; wonderful!" Is there a lesson here for the parents of small children?

FRIGID BOON / The modern enthusiasm for the deep-freeze interests me, but I am not in the forefront of the movement, for I have observed that quite a lot of frozen food has a taste of brown paper, and is not always completely unfrozen. I lost my appetite for snow and ice when I was a boy. But I feel that the real possibilities of the deep-freeze technique have not been explored. If it can halt decay and arrest all bodily processes, why can the machine not be used as a baby-tender? Consider: a week-end is being planned, and parents are wondering what they can do with the infant; aha! pop it in the deep-freeze, and thaw it out on Monday morning, unharmed and the better for a thorough rest. Junior is behaving badly at school; the family psychiatrist says that he is going through "a phase"; put him in the deep-freeze until the phase has run its course. An expectant mother, who adores the memory of Queen Victoria, is told that her offspring will be born about May 10th; she deep-freezes herself until midnight, May 23rd, and little Victoria Alexandrina makes her debut, (perhaps a little stiff and blue) on the great Queen's birthday. Deep-freezing may prove the boon of the age.

PANGS OF LEISURE / For the first time in several weeks I found myself this afternoon without anything to do. Of late I have suffered from congestion of the calendar; every hour of every day has been painfully crammed with duties and obligations. This afternoon I was free – free as a bird. But like a bewildered prisoner suddenly ejected from his dungeon I did not know how to use my liberty. I tried the TV, but the reception was terrible. I composed myself for a nap in my chair, but every five minutes or so I would leap up, wide awake, shouting, "All right! Don't strike me! I'll do it at once," – a horrible reflection of my life for the past six weeks. I tried a few light household tasks, but they were like work, and I wanted to avoid work. I thought of going for a walk, but the outer world was an indecisive mess of hail, snow, rain and fog. I paced up and down, pretending that I was thinking, but soon tired of it. By four o'clock I was almost frantic with leisure; if I did not find some pleasant way of loafing soon, my afternoon would be gone. And sure enough, it did go, and the jaws of duty closed on me again. Oh, the pity of it!

*

COMMUNIQUÉ (*scrawled in chalk on my front door*)

To Big Chief Marchbanks.

How, Marchbanks:

In awful trouble, Marchbanks. Winter come soon. I got to get in jail. Been out two week now. No jail, no winter home. Two day ago I get drunk. Sick on cop. He mad. Ha, I think; jail for sure. But no. He take pants to cleaner and make me work cutting wood to pay for clean pants. Yesterday I throw brick at cop. Hit him hard. He jump. Ha, I think; jail now. But he say thanks pal; sergeant coming and you just wake me up in time. This one hell country, Marchbanks. Cops all too mean to put poor Indian in jail.

How, again,
Osceola Thunderbelly,
Chief of the Crokinoles.

*

CULLED FROM THE APOPHTHEGMS
OF WIZARD MARCHBANKS

After 45 the differences which divide men from women are trivial compared with those which separate the wise from the unwise, the whole from the fragmented, the survivors from the fallen.

$2{\rm l}$ jupiter

Oscola Thunder
b. dec. 5 : 1878

Sagittarius

mutable, fiery

(November 23 to December 22)

SAGITTARIUS IS the sign of the Archer, the shooter of arrows or, if you prefer the phrase, the thrower of the harpoon. Your special gift is the knowledge of the power of the spoken word, and in particular the derogatory word. Persons of coarse fibre, born under this sign, may expend their gift in indiscriminate abuse, but the more intelligent Sagittarians husband their abilities and say no more than is absolutely necessary to discomfit or perhaps to explode their rivals. Those most highly developed of all are able to shoot their arrows (or throw their harpoons) with such grace that they seem to speak in positive praise of those they seek to destroy, as thus: "Yes, you have to admit that good old Taurus never does less than his best, even when he has completely missed the point;" or, "Virgo and I have been friends since we were girls, and if she can only overcome a few of those

* 142

nervous little ticks she may expect to marry as well as anyone."
People born under this sign often go a long way, though seldom
as far as their friends could wish.

Enchantment-of-the-Month

ᐳ✳᷼᳀᷻᳀ᐳ✳᷼᳀᷻᳀ᐳ✳᷼᳀᷻᳀ᐳ✳᷼᳀᷻᳀ᐳ✳᷼᳀᷻᳀᷼

Your lucky colours give you a reasonably free hand in dress;
they are black, blue, orange, sea-green, violet and purple. You
have only one lucky flower, according to astrologers, and that is
goldenrod. If you suffer from hay fever your luck will, of course,
consist in seeing as little of it as possible; it is always possible to
discover *something* lucky about everything; astrology is the
Pollyanna of the occult sciences. Your lucky gems are the tur-
quoise, diamond, emerald, amethyst and carbuncle. If the word
carbuncle conjures up memories of a painful lump some member
of your family once had, be at peace; the jewel is the garnet,
cut *en cabochon*. You will not, in all likelihood, have to worry
too much about lucky gems for Sagittarians are thought to be
romantic souls, and of such is the kingdom of the diamond
merchants. You are virtually certain either to receive a diamond,
or give one; when that important preliminary is over, you may
set about acquiring your other lucky gems at your leisure.

Health Hints for Those Born Under Sagittarius

If you have an affliction, it is likely to smite you hip and thigh,
for lumbago, sciatica and all the ills which make it hard to walk
are considered by astrologers to have a particular fancy for
people born at your time of the year. Painful as these troubles
are, they are excellent themes for conversation, and if you have
to do a lot of sitting, you will need something to talk about. You
may discuss them freely without embarrassing anyone; talk
about malignant or contagious diseases is likely to make your
friends uneasy, but nobody has ever caught lumbago from
another, and nobody ever thinks he will suffer from it until the
moment when it strikes. Therefore your afflictions will serve to
make you popular, for we always tend to like people who are
less fortunate than ourselves, particularly when we are not
called upon to do anything to lessen their misfortunes.

*

SWEETLY SOLEMN THOUGHTS

REMOVAL OF COUSINS / Listened to a family discussion among
some people who were trying to decide the relationship to

themselves of the children of a brother of their grandfather's second wife. It was perfectly clear to me, but they made a sad hash of it. The Welsh and the Scots are the only people who really understand the fine points of relationship, and I think that the Welsh have a slight edge on the Scots in this matter. Indeed, I have given some thought to writing a book on the subject with a special Appendix dealing with the Removal of Cousins. The number of people, apparently well-educated and intelligent, who cannot distinguish between a Second Cousin and a First Cousin Once Removed, is staggering and reflects unpleasantly on our educational system. What these poor softies do when they get into the flood-tide of genealogy, with Intermarriage of Cousins and Collateral Cousinship In The Second Generation, I dread to imagine.

CRITICS CRITICIZED / I always read newspaper criticisms of concerts I have attended, but often I wonder if the critic and I can have been at the same affair. It is not their discontent that puzzles me; tastes differ, and after all a critic's stock-in-trade is a finer sensibility than that of the vulgar herd. And I make allowances for the fact that going to concerts is work for a critic, and there are plenty of people who have lost all love for the work by which they get their bread. No, it is the way most of them write that stuns me. They attempt to deal with the performances of artists who have spent not less than ten years acquiring insight and a formidable technique, in a maimed and cretinous prose which could not possibly give anybody any impression except one of confusion and depleted vitality. They are poor grammarians, and their vocabularies are tawdry. It is hard enough to interpret one art in terms of another under the best of circumstances, but when the critic has not understood that writing also is an art, his criticism becomes embarrassing self-portraiture.

RESTAURANT COWARDICE / What is wrong with me? I seem to be the sort of man whom waiters immediately put at a table near the kitchen which smells of other people's food, or in a draught, or too near the orchestra, or someplace where nobody wants to sit. If anything is spilled, it is mine; if anything spilled is scraped up from the floor, and served with carpet-fluff in it, it is mine. Am I so broken a creature that I fear to make a row in a restaurant? Well, all the evidence points in that direction. I am even so base that I lack the courage to refuse when the waiter suggests that I eat something which I do not want. This evening, for instance, I was thus dragooned into eating a Greek sweetmeat called Baclava; it tasted like a Bible printed on India paper which had been thoroughly soaked in honey, and took just as long to eat. When I had chewed my way down to Revelation the waiter asked me if I had enjoyed it and I, spiritless wretch, managed to nod.

*

FROM THE MARCHBANKS MUNIMENTS

To Samuel Marchbanks, ESQ.

Dear and Valued Customer:

With a sensation of sick shock we find that you have not yet been in to do your Xmas shopping. Already the best of our stock is picked over and unless you hurry! Hurry!! HURRY!!! you will miss out on the finest array of Xmas yummies of all kinds that it has ever been our privilege and pleasure to stock.

Everything that you could possibly wish to give to a relative is to be found in our Pharmacy Department, and may be purchased by presenting a doctor's prescription. Many goods in this line may be secured by signing a simple statement that you want to poison a dog.

In our Jewellery displays we have every sort of simulated gem with which husband or lover could wish to simulate affection.

In our Gigantic Kiddyland we have no less than three Santa Clauses, which avoids much of the queuing to shake hands with the genial saint which has caused irritation among busy tots at past Christmases.

You owe it to yourself to do your Christmas shopping RIGHT NOW. Stop owing it to yourself. Owe it to us.

> J. Button Hook
> (For the Bon Ton Elite Shoppery)

*

To the Rev. Simon Goaste, B.D.

Dear Rector:

I suppose you have observed, in the course of your professional duties, the sad decline of literary exuberance in the writing of epitaphs? The modern epitaph is hardly worthy of the name, when one compares it with the great epitaph-writing of the eighteenth century.

Because I do not wish to be slighted on my tombstone, I am sending to you herewith my own epitaph, in order that you may circumvent any of my descendants or executors who want to do the thing on the cheap after I am gone.

145 *

Beneath this stone
Lies all that was Mortal
Of one
Who, in this transitory Life
Seemed to sum up in himself all those
Virtues
Which we are taught to admire
but which, alas,
We rarely see in action.

Pause, Passer-By and Ponder:

This man, beside an ample fortune for
Those Left to Mourn Him
Leaves a sum in trust to provide
Every child in this Parish
With copies of his own works
Durably bound in waterproof material,
As well as a medal bearing the impress of his
Noble Countenance
on the front, and on its rear
These Words:
'For Memorial Purposes only:
Not Negotiable as Currency.'

Drop a Tear and Pass On
Drawing Such Consolation As You Can
From the indisputable fact
that
We Shall Not Look Upon His Like Again.

There. I think that covers the ground pretty thoroughly, and will gladden the heart of the stone-mason, if not of my relatives. Oh yes, and on the top of the stone, please, an effigy of my own head, with the left eyelid drooping slightly, as though in salute to the living.

Yours cheerily,
Samuel Marchbanks.

*

To Amyas Pilgarlic, ESQ.

Dear Pil:

I have just been writing to Pastor Goaste about my epitaph. While I am clearing things up with regard to my funeral, permit me to inform you that among my gramophone records you will find one marked "For Pilgarlic only." This is my funeral eulogy.

When my funeral is arranged, I want you to have a large public address system in the church, and a record player. Then when the time comes for the usual address, play the record. You had better warn the parson beforehand, or there may be some competition.

The address is, I flatter myself, rather novel. I personally admonish several people who are sure to be at my funeral, and make a few remarks that I have been hankering to make all my life. I also give a brief estimate of my own character, which is more interesting than anything the parson can do, for it is founded on first-hand information. I expect that my action in this matter will set a new style.

Yours gaily,
Sam.

*

To Samuel Marchbanks, ESQ.

Dear Neighbour:

Aw, gee, I never thought you would mind me playing the hi-fi with my windows open! Aw, heck, I never thought you would resent a little thing like that skunk getting into your car! Not that I admit I did it. My lawyers told me that I shouldn't. But I never thought you'd go to court about it. Gee, Marchbanks, you're a cranky guy! Gee, haven't you any spirit of give and take?

I'm just sick about the whole thing, and so is Lambie-Pie. She says you're the worst crab in the world, but we ought to try to be friends with you because we're neighbours, and after all, even you are human. She says we got to extend the Right Hand of Fellowship. Consider it extended. How about it, Marchbanks, old pal? By the way, I borrowed your lawn mower last month when you were away. I accidentally ran it over a big bolt somebody dropped on my lawn. I'll bring it back just as soon as it is fixed. Or would you rather have it fixed to suit yourself?

Yours repentantly,
Dick Dandiprat.

*

To Richard Dandiprat, ESQ.

Unspeakable Dandiprat:

I take note that you have extended the Right Hand of Fellowship. I have examined it. Take it back and wash it.

My legal action against you continues according to plan. I shall also sue you for the damage to my lawnmower.

You may inform Lambie-Pie (whom I take to be your consort) that I am not human. I sprang, full-grown, from a riven oak one midnight many years ago.

Yours in a very limited sense,
Samuel Marchbanks.

*

To Raymond Cataplasm, M.D., F.R.C.P.

Dear Dr. Cataplasm:

I have met a good many people during the past two weeks who have wagged their heads dolefully and said, "A green Christmas makes a fat graveyard." As a physician and a man of science, do you think that this is true? Watching the way that some of them have been eating and drinking over the festive season I would be more inclined to say, "A fat Christmas makes a green graveyard."

How did the illusion grow up that cold winters are healthier than mild ones? Is it part of our Puritan insistence on the superiority of whatever is disagreeable and inconvenient? And can you tell me if the graveyards in Florida and California are especially fat? Personally I dislike the expression "fat graveyard"; it suggests that the earth of the graveyard is of a squelchy, suety, gustful, mince-meaty quality, with headstones stuck in it like blanched almonds in a plum pudding. An obscene fantasy, and one unbecoming such pure and airy spirits as yours and mine.

Your perennial patient,
S. Marchbanks.

*

To Samuel Marchbanks, ESQ.

Dear Marchbanks:

Will you lend me your Santa Claus costume? I want it for the annual party of the Rowanis Club, of which I am Grand Exalted Merrymaker this year. We are having a Christmas celebration, and I thought it would be an original idea if I dressed up as S.C. and gave everybody presents containing sneeze powder, white mice, dribble glasses and etc.

I hope you are not brooding about that little matter of the skunk? We have led the lawyers a fine dance, haven't we? Ha ha! Still, we are both men of the world, eh Marchbanks?

Will you send the S.C. suit to the cleaners right away, so that I can pick it up next week? I want to look well at the party, and those suits get pretty dirty when they are not taken care of.

Your neighbour,
Dick Dandiprat.

*

To Mouseman, Mouseman and Forcemeat.

Dear Mr. Mouseman:

I am going out of my mind! That misbegotten ruffian Dandiprat has just written me a letter in which he virtually confesses that he put the skunk in my car!

Now Mouseman, what can you do to Dandiprat? Don't talk to me about the gallows; it is too good for him. Is there a thumb-screw anywhere that we can borrow? Or what about the Chinese water torture? Should I ask my laundry man if he will co-operate? Or what do you say to Mussolini's merry prank with a quart of castor oil? I warn you, Mouseman, if I do not have revenge I shall drown in my own gall! Get to work at once.

Yours furiously,
S. Marchbanks.

*

REFLECTIONS

EPIDERMIS / A medical acquaintance mentioned idly that you can tell a good deal about the age of a human being by pinching the skin on the backs of the hands; according as it retains the shape of the pinch, the patient is advanced in decay. Spent much of the day pinching the skin on the backs of my hands, which snapped back into place very quickly at some points, and at others remained obstinately curled up. From this I conclude that my skin reflects the character of my opinions, some of which are young and fresh, and others far gone in senility.

FASHION IN KISSES / To the movies, and as I sat through a double feature I was interested to observe that the audible kiss has come back into fashion. When the first talking pictures appeared, kisses were all of the silent variety; it was just about then that silent plumbing made its first appearance, and there may have been some connection. But now the shadow-folk of Hollywood kiss with a noise like a cow pulling its foot out of deep mud. In my younger days there were two types of kiss: the Romantic Kiss was for private use and was as silent as the grave; the Courtesy Kiss, bestowed upon aunts, cousins and the like was noisy and wet, generally removing two square inches of mauve face powder. A visiting aunt, having been welcomed by two or three nephews, needed substantial repairs. The Romantic Kiss also involved closing the eyes, to indicate extreme depth of feeling, though it often occurred to me that if one cannot see what one is kissing, a pretty girl and a kid glove of good quality are completely indistinguishable.

CUT-RATE AUTOGRAPHS / Had an opportunity to examine a collection of autographs, and wondered once again what makes people collect them. The futility of collecting scraps of paper upon which people have scribbled (autograph-collecting) seems to me to be exceeded only by the futility of collecting scraps of paper which people have licked (stamp-collecting). There is a certain interest, perhaps, in the manner in which a great man signs his name, though not much. I would be delighted to own a page of manuscript written by Ben Jonson or Cardinal Bembo, for both were masterly calligraphers; but letters from most modern authors and statesmen are mere scribbles. In childhood most of us have a spell during which we carefully collect the autographs of our families, the milkman, the baker and the laundry man; then we lose the album. But I am surprised whenever I am reminded that the craze continues into adult life, and that great sums of money are spent on signatures of writers, musicians, criminals, politicians, and the like. I have a little skill in forgery, and I am thinking of going into a business where I shall undertake to provide a good facsimile of anybody's signature for twenty-five cents. Thus, for a modest sum, the eager collector will be able to get some rare items.

VALIANT FOR TRUTH / Received a letter from a cow, or it may simply have been from somebody who takes orders from a cow; I couldn't quite make out. It appears that when I made public my intention of keeping a cow in my cellar I suggested that cows shed their horns annually; the letter denied this. It is possible, though improbable, that I am wrong. I am not sure that I would know a cow if I met one. A certain cloudiness of vision, caused by long hours poring over the Scriptures, makes it impossible for me to identify an animal or even a human being at a distance of more than five feet. The cows which Santa Claus employs to draw his sleigh certainly have horns, for I have seen pictures of them. But if cows do not shed their horns, how comes it that cow horns are so plentiful? Cow horns are used to make horn-rimmed spectacles, snuff boxes for Scotsmen, powderhorns for outlaws, inkhorns for scholars, horns for automobiles, and for a variety of purposes. Am I expected to believe that all these horns come from dead cows and represent a lifetime of patient horn-growing? No, no, I am not so foolish as that. Until I am shown otherwise I shall believe that cows shed their horns each Spring.

*

To Raymond Cataplasm, M.D., F.R.C.P.

Dear Dr. Cataplasm:

The other day I read the autobiography of an Armenian gentleman named Nubar Gulbenkian; he hopes to live as long as his grandfather, who died at the age of 106. The book described this ancient's meals in detail. Two facts about them impressed me; each meal (he ate four times a day) took 45 minutes; each meal ended with a plate of Turkish sweets.

I have never taken 45 minutes to eat a meal in my life. I can eat eight courses in fifteen minutes. Can it be that I eat too fast for long life and health?

I detest Turkish sweets. They appear to me to be made of raw mutton fat into which low-caste Turks have ground caraway seeds by rubbing it between the soles of their feet.

However, Gulbenkian eats slowly and he eats nasty things, and he expects to achieve a great age. Perhaps you would like to quote his example to a few patients who are not so hasty and fastidious as,

Your perennial patient,
Samuel Marchbanks.

*

To Amyas Pilgarlic, ESQ.

Dear Pil:

A few days ago I visited Toyland, as I do every year, just to see how the Christmas Racket is getting along. Toyland is as hot as ever; the temperature was not a smidgeon under 90°F. Most of the customers, like myself, wore full Winter outdoor dress, and were suffering hideously. The only really comfortable people appeared to be the gnomes and elves who were helping Santa; these were young women ranging from the toothsome to the merely wholesome, dressed in shirts and very short shorts. This association between Santa Clause and the female underpinning fascinated me; Santa was there for the children, but the gnomes were there for the fathers – in a very limited sense, of course.

Santa himself, beneath his paint and ample white beard, seemed to be about 25; when children approached him his eyes rolled in an agonized fashion which betrayed the youthful bachelor. A photographer was on the spot, assisted by a leggy female gnome, taking pictures of every tot with Santa. This impressed me as a fine stroke of commercial whimsy, and I started up the runway myself. "Where you goin'?" said a blonde gnome with a large bust, catching me by the arm. "To have my picture taken with Santa," said I. "It's just for the kids," said she, trembling a little and looking for the manager. "I am a child at heart, gnome," said I. But she had pressed a button in the wall beside her, and at this moment a store detective appeared, wearing the insensitive expression of his kind. "What gives?" said he. "This character wants to go up the runway with the kids," said the gnome. "Oh, one of them sex-monsters eh?" said the detective, closing one eye in a menacing fashion. For a moment I feared that I might have to spend Christmas in jail with my friend Osceola Thunderbelly. But I talked my way out of it, and as I hastened away the detective gave the gnome a slap on the podex which was probably mere brotherly goodwill. Christmas is becoming a terribly complicated season, full of mixed and mistaken motives.

Yours, still blushing at the shame of it,
Sam.

*

To Raymond Cataplasm, M.D., F.R.C.P.

Dear Dr. Cataplasm:

It was most kind of you to send me a Christmas card. It is a beautiful thing, and I shall probably have it framed. By the way, what is it? I did not know that you were interested in modern art.

Yours gratefully,
S. Marchbanks.

P.S. How foolish of me! I have been looking at your card upside down. Of course it is a lovely photograph of autumn colours.
S.M.

*

To Samuel Marchbanks, ESQ.

Dear Mr. Marchbanks:

Through some oversight my secretary has sent you a coloured transparency representing a drunkard's liver, in mistake for a Christmas card. If you will return it, a card showing myself and Mrs. Cataplasm on the verandah of our Summer home will be sent to you at once.

Yours sincerely,
Raymond Cataplasm.

*

To Samuel Marchbanks, ESQ.

Dear Marchbanks:

No card from you this year. Surely our little fuss with lawyers is not going to cause a breach between us?

Can I borrow your bladder for a New Year party? I mean the one you put on the table under a dinner plate and then pump up secretly, making the plate jump. You never seemed to use it effectively, and I know I could be the life of the party with it. Just leave it in the hall and I'll pick it up.

Yours forgivingly,
Dick Dandiprat.

*

To Richard Dandiprat, ESQ.

Sir:

You will hear from my lawyers, if they ever get around to it, which seems doubtful. I did not send you a card because I loathe and despise you.

My bladder is not yours to command. I have plans for a Happy New Year which require it.

An evil, ill-starred New Year to you and yours.
S. Marchbanks.

*

To Samuel Marchbanks, ESQ.

Dear Sam:

From time to time I am moved to wonder where people get their ideas about food. Last night, for instance, I dined with friends, whom I took to be persons of some discrimination. But – I scarcely expect to be believed, though I vow that it is true – the last thing on the menu was halves of grapefruit which had been lightly boiled, and over which creme de menthe had been poured! I ate it, because I am a polite person and always eat what is set before me, but when I say that my gorge rose I am not employing a mere idle form of words. When, at last, I got out into the cold night air I allowed my gorge to rise all the way, after which I felt much better. – It is such trials, I suppose, that give us strength for even greater calamities, if greater calamities than boiled, booze-drenched grapefruit can be.

I hope the New Year will not use you too hardly.
Amyas Pilgarlic.

*

To Mrs. Kedijah Scissorbill.

Dear Mrs. Scissorbill:

Because I am a great admirer of novelty in any form, I write to congratulate you on your most successful performance as Santa Claus at the Christmas party which your club, The Militant Female Society, gave for the Misbegotten Orphans.

As you said in your speech to the Orphans, there is no reason whatever why Santa Claus should not be a woman. And I thought your costume and makeup excellent. It was a fine idea to wear your own abundant grey hair, loose and hanging down your back. This made up for the lack of the long beard which we associate with S. Claus. I think you would be wise another time to put some fire-proofing on your hair; I observed one well-developed male orphan, with quite a moustache, testing it with his cigarette-lighter. I think, too, that your pince-nez, and the natural austerity of your countenance, gave Santa an authority he sometimes lacks.

Altogether, it was a triumph, and I expect that the craze for female Santas will sweep the country.

Yours respectfully,
Samuel Marchbanks.

*

To Miss Minerva Hawser.

Dear Miss Hawser:

It is all very well for you to write to me on Dec. 23rd, asking for a Christmas play which you can rehearse and present on Dec. 25th, but it imposes a strain on my invention. If your Sunday School group wants a play from my hand, this is the best I can do for them; I am not sure that it is entirely suited to a class of girls between 8 and 10 years of age, but you must do your best, as I have done mine.

THE RIVAL SANTAS
A CHRISTMAS DRAMA
by
Samuel Marchbanks

The curtain rises (or, if I know Sunday school stages, jerks painfully apart) to reveal a richly furnished drawing-room with a fireplace (indicated by some chairs from the vestry and a packing case decorated with red crepe paper). The sound of sleigh-bells is heard, then a few buckets of soot burst from the fireplace, followed by Santa Claus; he has a sack of toys on his back.

* 154

SANTA: Ho, ho, ho! Oh what a jolly old fellow I am. Ho, ho, ho! (*He brushes his clothes, knocking a lot of soot into the front rows of the audience.*) I am welcome everywhere. Nobody has ever breathed a word of criticism against me. Ho, ho, ho!

A VOICE: Stop saying Ho, ho, ho!

SANTA: Who said that?

A VOICE: I did.

SANTA: Who are you?

A VOICE: I'm St. Nicholas, that's who.

SANTA: Go on! I'm St. Nicholas myself.

A VOICE: Have you any papers to show it?

SANTA: I don't need papers. It's a Well-Known Fact. Come on out and let me see you. (*An old man in the robes of a mediaeval bishop enters the room (remind him not to trip over his crozier); he looks rather like Santa, but more intelligent and grouchy. He has on a long blue cloak, with fur on it. He is St. Nicholas.*)

SANTA: Well, you're a fine-looking old spook. Do you live here?

ST. NICK: You're no Beauty Queen yourself. No: I'm a spirit and on Christmas Eve I wander the earth, doing good.

SANTA: Funny I've never heard of you. Come to think of it, I don't remember ever seeing your picture on a magazine cover or an advertisement.

ST. NICK: I'm not always shoving myself forward, like Some People I Could Mention.

SANTA: Meaning me?

ST. NICK: If the cap fits, wear it.

SANTA: Now look here, I don't want any trouble. I'm a popular spirit and I have my public. Little children love me. Storekeepers love me. Manufacturers love me. Everybody who is anybody loves me.

ST. NICK: Do parents love you?

SANTA: I suppose so. Parents love everything that is good for their children. If they don't the children make them. You don't understand what a force children are in the modern world.

ST. NICK: Who do you think you're talking to? I'm the patron saint of children.

SANTA: You need a refresher course in child psychology.

ST. NICK: Do you know what I think? I think you're the most egotistical old spirit I've ever met. Do you know why you're so popular with children? Because children are egotists too. So you and little children love each other, eh? Ha Ha! Birds of a feather.

SANTA: That's fine talk for a saint. You're disgruntled and jealous of my popularity, that's all. Next thing you'll be smoking up

155 *

to parents, trying to convince them that they have some
share in Christmas.

ST. NICK: Yes, I will. I'll promote a Parents' League For the
Reform of Christmas. No more indigestible food, no more
noise, no more paper hats, no more mica snow getting up
your nose. Just a quiet day at home with a jug.

SANTA: You're a reactionary!

ST. NICK: You're a Red!

SANTA: I am not!

ST. NICK: Yes you are; you've even got a red suit on!

SANTA: Those are fighting words! (*He swings at St. Nick with
his bag of toys: St. Nick cracks him over the head with his
crozier. As they fight the Spirit of Christmas is lowered from
above the stage on a wire. She should be a skinny little girl
with frizzled hair and a fairy wand.*)

SPT. OF CH.:   Oh, do not fight
                On Christmas night;
                Nor air your peeve
                On Christmas Eve.
                Silent night
                Holy night
                Saints should know
                It's wrong to fight.

(*St. Nick, who cannot stand her voice a moment longer, kicks
the Spirit of Christmas hard on the caboose. She screams,
and spins rapidly on her wire. As she whirls she gores Santa's
stomach with her wand and two old sofa cushions from the
Rectory fall out. Amid general confusion the curtain falls.*)

You may find that some people will not like this play; they will
say that it does not reflect the true Christmas Spirit. Tell them
from me that if they think they can do better at short notice to
go ahead.

> Yours in the Yuletide Spirit,
> S. Marchbanks.

*

To Amyas Pilgarlic, ESQ.

Dear Pil:

On Christmas Eve it is surely not indiscreet of me to confide
the secrets of my Christmas List to you. As I told you earlier, I
am giving Canadiana this year. Here is the list:

Uncle Fortunatus: an old drum, almost certainly used by troops
in the 1837 rebellion. Both heads are gone, but can be easily

replaced. All the decoration and regimental ornament have been worn, or rusted, away, but a skilful restorer could put them back again if we knew what they were. Spiteful people say it is an old cheese-box, but I have the true collector's flair, and know it is a drum. Uncle will love it.

Brother Fairchild: an old Quebec heater, almost certainly the one around which the Fathers of Confederation sat when planning the future of this great Dominion. Who can say what historic spit may not cling to it? It is, in the truest sense, a shrine. As a stove, of course, it has seen its best days. Fairchild will be delighted.

Cousin Ghengis: A flag, used by a militia regiment which set out to quell the Riel Rebellion, but was detained in one of the bars in Toronto. It is a most interesting piece of work, which shows signs of having been an Orange Lodge banner before it was converted to its later purpose. It is rather stained with something which might be blood, though an analytical chemist says it still smells of whisky. Ghengis will be ecstatic.

Nephew Gobemouche: a stamp used by a Member of Parliament in mailing a letter from the Parliament Buildings. Such stamps are exceedingly rare, and a few philatelists deny that any genuine examples are in existence. I happen to know, however, that on September 12, 1896, the franking-machine was out of order for a few hours, and free stamps were given to members at the Parliamentary Post Office. Gobemouche will be tearful with pleasure.

Nephew Belial: a horn from Laura Secord's famous cow. When blown it emits a musty smell but no sound. Belial will be livid.

And as for you, my dear friend – but no; you must wait until tomorrow to see what I have sent you.

A Merry Christmas!

Sam.

*

REFLECTIONS

IMPERFECT GROOMING / Met a man who, in casual conversation, referred to someone we both knew as "the sort of fellow who has never found out that you really can't make a shirt do for more than one day." This depressed me. I am always depressed in the presence of those who wear a clean shirt every day, bathe every day, never drop food on their fronts and always have their shoes shined and their trousers creased. I would fain be one of them.

But alas, I never seem to be attending to what I am doing when I dress. Absent-mindedly I snatch whatever comes to hand; sometimes the effect is of a stunning elegance; more often it is not. If I bathe every day, especially in Winter, I develop a kind of all-over dandruff, and raw patches appear on my hide. I would love to be so clean that my presence was a reproach to lesser men, but I am not. I am not spectacularly dirty, either. I am just one of those people who has never completely convinced himself that a shirt will not do for more than one day. I comfort myself that in this I resemble Dr. Johnson, who only changed his shirt when his friends presented him with a petition; but alas, I have not the courage or determination to resemble him closely.

LET THE EAR JUDGE / Somebody in the States, I see, has conceived the notion of recording classics of literature on long-playing records. After listening to such a recording it would no longer be necessary to go through the fatigue of reading the *Iliad*, the *Odyssey*, *Paradise Lost*, the *Divine Comedy*, or any other exhausting work. It must be said for such a scheme that it would restore the ear as the first judge of poetry, and expose that false judge, the eye. But I doubt if many people would hear the great works often enough to get near the root of them.

CHRISTMAS CHEER / Finished my Christmas shopping. True, I finished it three weeks ago, but it is a job which I find requires finishing more than once. At the end of November I fought, bit and clawed my way through the shops, battling with savage women and bitten in the leg by cannibal children, and gathered enough assorted rubbish to fill, as I thought, my Christmas needs. But in the light of Christmas Week it has proved to be too little; my bosom is inflated, nigh to bursting, with Brotherly Love and eggnog, and today I sallied forth to shop again. The shops were almost empty, and although the clerks were a little vague and tended to hiccup when asked questions, I achieved my wishes in a short time and hurried home to decorate my tree. Preparatory to this task I nogged a couple of dozen eggs, and when visitors dropped in I was able to offer them a drink of the plushy, caressing fluid which does so much to take the bitterness out of Christmas. . . . I have made my own angel for the top of the Christmas tree. As a delineator of the female form I tend to express myself in unmistakable terms; I like even an angel to appear as if she had some fun in her. In consequence my angel looks a little like Diana of the Ephesians, what with eggnog and one thing and another.

CHRISTMAS MERRYMAKING
(*a bonus for party-loving readers of the Almanack*)

NOTHING SERVES to break the ice at Christmas so effectively as a good-humoured hoax or imposture perpetrated by some quick-witted member of the company upon an unsuspecting fellow guest. You may play the coveted role of wit, and earn the gratitude of your hostess, by thoroughly mastering the following simple, but effective jests.

Showing him your fountain pen, induce a fellow-guest to wager that it will not write any colour he cares to name. When he says (for example) "Green," reveal nothing by your countenance but write the letters g-r-e-e-n upon a sheet of paper. Then appeal to the company at large as to whether you have not won your wager. His stupefaction will be very laughable. (If you are a lady, of course, you will wager half-a-dozen pairs of gloves rather than a sum of money.)

Another eminently "practical" joke is this: say to a fellow-guest (whom you have previously ascertained to be a philatelist) "Pardon me, sir (or if you are acquainted with him, "Colonel A," or "Judge B") but is it true that you collect stamps?" When he says "Yes," bring your right shoe smartly down upon his left instep (or *vice versa* if you happen to be left-handed), saying at the same time, "Capital! collect *this* one!" Whatever his feelings may be, the laughter of the company will certainly give him his cue to take this as a good joke upon himself, for no true gentleman wishes to be a spoilsport, embarrassing his hostess and clouding the delight of the company. (If a lady, be sure that you bring the *heel* of your shoe upon the instep of your "victim," as you may otherwise turn your ankle and be forced to send for your carriage.)

*

COMMUNIQUÉ (*by ordinary surface mail but unstamped*)

To Big Chief Marchbanks.

How, Marchbanks:

This one hell country, Marchbanks. No place for honest man. Listen. Last week I no money. Christmas come. I good Indian, Marchbanks. Baptized lots of times. Want to do right by Gitche Manitou on he birthday. Want for buy case lilac hair juice for drink Gitche Manitou health on birthday. No money. Every place Christmas shopper. All spend. All sad face. All think selfs happy. So I think I sell Christmas trees. One place I see plenty little trees. All blue. I get hatchet and cut down four. Then woman come to door of house. She say what I do? I say cut Christmas trees. Thief, she say – awful loud voice, Marchbanks, for skinny woman – I call cops. You cut my blue spruce. I grab trees. I run. Soon cops come in white car. Hey you, say cops. What you do in white car, I say. Sell ice cream, maybe. Ha! Joke, Marchbanks. Cops mad. So mad they get out of car. That awful mad for cop, Marchbanks. Take me police court. Little fellow at desk he say I been drinking. How I drink, I say, with no money. Little fellow belch. He been drinking Marchbanks. I smell. Jail ten days he say, and belch again. I belch too, for show polite, Indian style. Another ten days for contempt, he say. This one hell country, Marchbanks.

> Osceola Thunderbelly,
> Chief of the Crokinoles.

*

CULLED FROM THE APOPHTHEGMS
OF WIZARD MARCHBANKS

To judge from the number of books on the subject, it is easy for us to achieve the spiritual grandeur of Orientals by adopting their postures and systems of breathing. Oddly enough, no Orientals appear to believe that they can develop our scientific and governmental skill by posturing and breathing like *us*.

*

Saturn

Amyas Pilgarlic
b. Dec. 25, 1912.

Capricorn

an earthy sign

(December 23 to January 20)

CAPRICORN IS the sign of the Goat, but this is not as bad as it sounds. There always has to be a goat, and if the obvious goat plays his cards skilfully, popularity, promotion and success await him. The secret of being the goat lies in these words: Never deny and never protest. Anticipate blame. When something goes wrong and everyone else is trying to show that they could not possibly have been responsible for it, say coolly and frankly: "It's my fault; I wasn't here when it happened, but I should have foreseen it, and if anybody has to take the responsibility, let it be me." This will work like magic, and those who have been trying to escape blame will experience an indefinable sense that you have out-generaled them. Follow this course *always*, and with special firmness when you are obviously not to blame. Little by little an impression will spread that you are unaffected, fearless, ruthlessly honest and devoted to your job rather than to personal advancement. For female Capricorns this is the secret of happiness in marriage. A wife who is always to blame is prized above rubies, as Wizard Solomon said.

Enchantment-of-the-Month

Bad luck for you in the matter of lucky colours; your only good one is purple, and the others are grey, green, black and brown; you will need a lot of imagination to present a festive appearance in those. Your lucky flowers are the poppy, flax and holly. Your lucky gems are the onyx, the garnet, the sapphire and the amethyst, but the best of them all is the lodestone. Unfortunately this is simply magnetic oxide of iron, and it is not easy to make it into a pleasing adornment; even the genius of Fabergé was stumped by it. When once the late Czar Nicholas commissioned the celebrated jeweller to create a suitable gift for an Imperial favourite who was a Capricornian, Fabergé was unable to produce anything handsomer than an ordinary magnet with a golden handle, for a lodestone is simply a magnet. However, there is luck in everything; you can do your shopping at the hardware store instead of at the jeweller's, and a corsage of holly, held in place with a small magnet, will set you up for a big night of romance.

Health Hints for Those Born Under Capricorn

You have no special point of weakness, and are supposedly gifted with an iron constitution. Remember, your astrological sign is that of the goat, and goats are not given to fits of the vapours (not in the Victorian acceptance of the word, that is to say) and have never been pernickety about their food. But there must be reason in everything. You must not push your goatishness too far. Even a goat can ruin its constitution, though I cannot tell you how this is done. Nobody has ever seen a nauseated goat, or a drunk goat, and three veterinarians of long experience have assured me on their solemn oath that they have never seen a dead goat. However, as goats are mortal, they must be the inheritors of some of the ills of flesh, and my personal belief is that these are so dreadful that goats cannot bring themselves to speak of them. There is a look in the eye of certain elderly goats which tells a vague but hideous story. It looks like Disillusion, but is probably thirty-third degree ulcers.

*

FROM MY CHRISTMAS FILES

To Samuel Marchbanks, ESQ.

> *(Written on a card bearing the message 'A Merry Christmas and Good Wishes for 1949': the date has been altered in pencil to the current year.)*

Dear Nephew:

Thank you for your thoughtful present. I opened it, as you suggested, as soon as it arrived, and a prettier parcel of soap I have never seen. I shall distribute new cakes on Christmas morning to the whole household. Your notion of a cake of soap fashioned in the likeness of an Aberdeen terrier for your Uncle Gomeril will flatter his Scottish susceptibilities.

I already have quite a number of gifts to be returned and exchanged as soon as the shops open after Christmas. Someone has thoughtlessly sent your Uncle a dressing-gown in the tartan of a clan from which the Marchbanks have been estranged for over three hundred years. He very sensibly asks what need he has of even an acceptable dressing-gown? He never wears one, and goes to his bath lightly wrapped in an old copy of the Toronto *Globe*, the Scotsman's friend.

> Your affct. aunt,
> Bathsheba Marchbanks.

*

To Samuel Marchbanks, ESQ.

> *(Written on an expensive but aesthetically reprehensible card which reveals a robin sitting on a bare branch, with a twig of holly in its beak; the bird's eye is a black bead, and the holly berries are red beads, cleverly glued to the paper. Spelled out in twigs of holly and mistletoe is the message: 'Just the Old, Old Wish.')*

Dear Mr. Marchbanks:

I had hoped that this seasonable greeting might come from Mrs. Wittol as well as myself, but she has been absent from home for several days. I have not heard from her, but last night a man's voice on the phone made some very insulting remarks to me, and I thought I recognized her hiccup among the background noises.

> Yours regretfully,
> Waghorn Wittol.

*

To Samuel Marchbanks, ESQ.

(Written upon a card which bears a portrait of Santa Claus, wearing an expression possible only to one drunk, or mad; realism has been added to the picture by a feather, glued on to represent the Saint's beard.)

At this gladsome tide I and Lambie-Pie hasten to freely offer yet once again the right hand of fellowship which you have so often spurned. As the angel's message of Peace on Earth, Goodwill Toward Men rings round the sad old world I beseech you to drop your legal action against me for hiding a skunk in your car, and as Ye Goode Shippe NEW YEAR sets forth into uncharted seas of Time let the olive branch, symbol of neighbourly amity, wave freely from the poop.

Your repentant neighbour,
    Dick Dandiprat.

*

To Raymond Cataplasm, M.D., F.R.C.P.

(On a Greetings Telegram)

HAVE BEGUN FESTIVITIES EARLIER THAN EXPECTED STOP HASTEN WITH STOMACH PUMP STOP THINK SELF POISONED THREE DINNERS STILL TO GO STOP MERRY CHRISTMAS STOP
    MARCHBANKS

*

To Genghis Marchbanks, ESQ.

My Dear Cousin:
    I really think your terms are ungenerous, considering the season of the year. If, as you suggest, I bring all the unwanted Christmas presents I receive to your pawnshop, I shall expect more than a mere one-third of their ordinary retail price. I hate to say it, Genghis, but I do not consider that you are showing the Christmas Spirit. You can skin the public, if you like, but you ought to draw the line at skinning a relative.

Yours reproachfully,
    S. M.

*

To Samuel Marchbanks, ESQ.

My very dear Mr. Marchbanks:
    It has never been the custom of Mouseman, Mouseman and Forcemeat to send out greeting cards at the Festive Season; to a firm as old as ours such conduct would seem flashy. We do, however, send letters bearing good wishes to our more valued clients, of whom you, my dear sir, are not the least.

All of the firm are, I am happy to say, well. The life of our senior partner, Mr. Jabez Mouseman, has been considerably brightened since he began – through what scientific accident we know not – to receive television programs on his hearing-aid. When reception is particularly strong phantoms of charming young women in low-cut evening gowns may be seen to move gracefully across his shirt-bosom; at first Mr. Jabez thought himself beset by evil spirits, but now he spends many hours each day happily regarding himself in the mirror.

Mr. Cicero Forcemeat·is, as always, in rude health and his powerful voice – that boon of the successful advocate – is, if anything, stronger than before. His peroration in a divorce case last week cracked a chandelier in the court-room.

I am as always in good health and beg to subscribe myself, dear Mr. Marchbanks, with no legal qualification whatever, your servant and sincere well-wisher,

Mordecai Mouseman
(for Mouseman, Mouseman and Forcemeat).

*

To Samuel Marchbanks, ESQ.

Dear Sir:

This department finds that in computing your Income Tax for 1963 you neglected to mention that when you addressed the Ladies Arts and Letters Club of Pelvis, Sask., in that year you were treated by the committee to a dinner which cost $1.25. This constitutes hidden income, and you must pay tax amounting to 67 cents, plus extra tax for late payment, amounting to 9 cents, making 76 cents in all, within ten days or we shall pursue you with the full rigour of the law.

This Department has received a card from you bearing Christmas Greetings. We are returning the card which is the wrong size for our files, and enclose herewith proper forms for the expression of this wish, to be completed in triplicate, and returned at once.

Yours, but not as much as you are ours,
Haubergeon Hydra.

*

To Samuel Marchbanks, ESQ.

(A greeting card, obviously home made, to which has been glued a snapshot of a stringy female of cheerful aspect, nursing what looks like a very old floor mop.)

Yuletide Greetings from self and dearest Fido.
Minerva Hawser.

*

To Big Chief Marchbanks.

> *(An exceedingly dirty and crumpled picture of an ample lady of brilliant complexion, showing a lot of leg, and smoking a cigar.)*

How, Marchbanks:

Find this picture in top of cigar box. Make nice card for you. All us fellows in jail send you happy wishes. Warden promise good Christmas in jail. Chicken and mince pie. No women, he say. We need women. You got any women?

> Osceola Thunderbelly
> (Chief of the Crokinoles).

*

HOLIDAY REFLECTIONS

NO ROAST OX, THANKS / New Year's Day, and I hail the onset of another year by eating more than I should but not quite so much as I want. I yearn for the spacious days of the Middle Ages, when cooking was cooking. Those were the days when the lord of the manor was faced, at dinner, with a whole ox into which was stuffed a whole boar, into which was stuffed a lamb, into which was stuffed a hare, into which was stuffed a pheasant. When he had settled this difficult problem in carving, the lord ate the pheasant, and threw the wrappings to the scurvy knaves and lubberly churls who composed his household, and set to work on a venison pie and five or six pounds of mincemeat encased in marchpane. Only, if I had lived in the Middle Ages, I would undoubtedly have been a lubberly churl – or at best Pynne-Heade, the household jester – and would have had to eat over-cooked ox, swilled down with the water in which the mead-horns had been washed. I have no illusions about the glory of my ancestry. So I dismissed my dream of mediaeval gluttony, and picked at a few pounds of turkey and ham, and washed it all down with liquids so innocent that even the Government puts its stamp upon them.

A VULGAR ERROR / There is a widespread belief that all tobacco chewers are good spitters. I heard a friend talking today in a manner which showed that he subscribed to this superstition. But I know it to be false. In my childhood I used to spend much of my spare time around a blacksmith shop, and although some good spitting could be seen, most of it was poor. I have seen men – tobacco chewers of a quarter century's standing – who could not hit anything, and sometimes failed to clear their own chins.

I have seen chewers at that blacksmith's shop spit at a crack for an hour, without hitting it once. De Quincey writes that the London hackney-coachmen of his day were so accomplished that they could spit around a corner, but I do not believe it. De Quincey was a dope fiend, and nothing that he says can be accepted as evidence. Show me one of these virtuoso spitters, and I may change my mind. But not until then.

THE INIQUITY OF FREE BOOKS / There is a great rejoicing in some parts of Ontario because the provincial government has decided to give free school-books to children, but I am not among the merry-makers. I am a writer of books myself, and any move which inculcates in children the idea that books are things which you get for nothing excites my implacable enmity. There are too many free books already, in public libraries and other institutions primarily designed to rob authors of their livelihood. A pox on the memory of Andrew Carnegie and his misplaced benevolence! There are in Canada, by actual count, 528 people who buy books for their own use; an author may count on these people buying a copy of any book he writes. There are 6,417,333 people who are on friendly terms with the 528, and they all borrow their copies of new books, read them, and then write to the author, pointing out typographical errors, plagiarisms from Holy Writ, faulty economics, and other blemishes. If the Ontario Government is going to teach children that books drop from Heaven, or are supplied from the public purse, like wheat subsidies, the profession of letters in Canada will drop below that of the nightsoil removers.

*

FROM THE MARCHBANKS ARCHIVE

To Amyas Pilgarlic, ESQ.

Dear Pil:

I was at a Twelfth Night party last night – a wonderful affair. I haven't much use for people who confine their merry-makings to Christmas Day; I insist on the full Twelve Days of Christmas from The Day itself to Epiphany. There was a man at the party who had some snuff, and as we all took tentative, apprehensive pinches he told us that he had acquired the habit while fighting in the East with Ghurka troops. A Scotch officer, he said, had asked for a large tin of snuff to be sent to him from home and in due course it was dropped from a plane in a package with other supplies. But he never got it. The kitchen troops got it, and not understanding its use and assuming that it was some rare condiment they curried their meat with it. The result was such fires in the tripes as were never known before in the Chindits.

During the course of the evening several Scots reels were performed with more spirit than science on the part of most of the dancers. As I watched it struck me that the Canadians present might well have done a folk-dance of their own; folk dances can be easily faked. A little nimble bobbing about, a little clapping of the hands, a little playful running at the ladies and then retreating from them in fright, and a final prance round the room in which everybody bashes into everybody else – and there's your folkdance. I am working on one now, to be called "Marchbanks' Brawl."

Yours Januwearily,
Sam.

*

To the Rev. Simon Goaste, B.D.

Dear Rector:

Can you tell me why it is that so many brides insist on having the Bridal Chorus from Wagner's *Lohengrin* played as they stumble up the aisle at their weddings? It seems to me to be a singularly ill-chosen piece of music for such an occasion.

Consider the story of the opera: Elsa, a silly girl, has got herself into a mess; a young man comes along and very competently gets her out of it; he marries her, on the understanding that she will never ask his name or whence he comes; but Elsa and her relatives nag him insufferably until he can bear it no more, and leaves her. The lesson of the whole opera is that nosiness is a first-class way to break up a marriage, and Wagner, who was married to one of the great snoops of his time, knew what he was talking about. Why is it that girls want this prelude to a strikingly unfortunate marriage played at their weddings?

I have often wondered what happened to Elsa after Lohengrin ran away. My guess is that she set up in business as a Wronged Wife, forgot completely her part in breaking up her marriage, and passed her time very pleasantly at tea parties, warning younger women that Men Are Not To Be Trusted. What are your views?

Faithfully,
S. Marchbanks.

*

To Raymond Cataplasm, M.D., F.R.C.P.

Dear Dr. Cataplasm:

I was at a party recently where a lady was explaining a new medical theory to me, in which she said that her husband (who is a physician) is keenly interested. The nubbin of the theory is that placid and careful living is just as aging as rowdy living if you make a habit of it, and that the human metabolism needs frequent shocks, just to keep it on its toes, so to speak. For this reason everybody should take care to overeat grossly every now and then, or get drunk, or run a mile, or chop a cord of wood. Anything will do, so long as it is something to which the body is unaccustomed.

I have been testing this notion myself. You know that I will do anything to further the ends of science. I overate as much as possible all during the Christmas season, and washed the food down with strong waters. Result: except for a slight feeling of other-worldliness before breakfast I felt fine, and my metabolism chugged away like a Coin Wash. But during the past week I have run to and from my office, carrying a heavily-weighted briefcase, four times each day. Result: my metabolism has seized up, my circulation is at a stand-still, and I see everything upside down unless I keep a firm hold on the top of my head.

Undoubtedly there is a great lesson for science in this. Perhaps you will explain to me what it is. Meanwhile I am going to lie down.

Your perennial patient,

SAMUEL MARCHBANKS.

*

To Miss Minerva Hawser.

Dear Miss Hawser:

Thank you for your letter; if you really want my old Christmas cards, you can have them; your idea for cutting them up into bits and distributing them for use as confetti at the weddings of the Underprivileged seems to me to be an excellent one, and an accurate reflection of your kindly and ingenious nature. My cards may be a disappointment to you. They were classifiable under the following heads:

Ghastly Good Taste: plain white cards made of hard stuff like the icing of a Christmas cake, with an engraved greeting on them; indistinguishable from old-fashioned death notices.

Art Drearies: designed by people who are determined to get away from conventional Christmas colours and designs;

they are usually executed in shades suggesting cheese
mould. Some are religious, in a strictly 'God-is-dead' sense.

Stark Realism: cards to which snapshots of the senders have
been pasted, showing them at their worst, and often in
company with dead fish, half-dead dogs, and the like.

Canadian Art: showing the same French-Canadian farmer,
driving the same sleigh through the same bluish snow, but
in slightly different stages of his progress toward a village
consisting of a Church and three huts.

Phoney Mediaeval: showing people eating and drinking and
playing oversize guitars, and looking cleaner and healthier
than was likely in the Middle Ages.

Unspeakables: on which a reindeer with a red nose is depicted.

I sent cards in all these forms myself, for there was nothing
else to be had. But I really long for a decent old-fashioned
Christmas card, with the Virgin and Child on it, and Santa
Claus and his reindeer, and a robin with a twig of holly in its
beak, and some mica clinging to it to simulate snow, and a really
compendious and warm-hearted greeting in the manner of
G. K. Chesterton:

> Here's for a bursting Yuletide
> To my friends wherever they be!
> With boozing and stuffing
> And praying and puffing
> All under the Evergreen Tree!

Yours sincerely,
Samuel Marchbanks.

*

To Amyas Pilgarlic, ESQ.

Dear Pil:

Last night I was at the movies, and as usual it was necessary
to sit through a good deal of rather depressing stuff before we
were allowed to see the film which had really brought us to the
theatre. Among these shorts (why do you suppose they call
them shorts? Surely shortness is a comparative thing? Judged by
the anguish of spirit they induced, these affairs were immeasur-
ably long) – but as I was saying, among these shorts was one in
which the audience was asked to join in the singing of popular
gems of modern minstrelsy. But the audience refrained from
doing so, and sat in a glum and resentful silence until the short
had dragged out its weary length.

This is a hopeful sign. Human beings are refusing to be
cajoled into doing silly things by machines, and by celluloid

shadows. For a group of people to sing because a movie machine asks them to do so is just nonsense, and they know it.

Mark my words, the revolution of Man against Machine is close at hand, and when it comes we shall see the end of that era which historians are already referring to in learned works as The Age of Boloney.

Adieu,
    Sam.

*

FROM MY NOTE-BOOK

A BORE IN TRAINING / Talking to a young man I realized, with a shock, that in fifteen years he would be a bore. The young are never bores, though they are often boring, particularly when they talk about themselves. But it does not lie in the power of youth to be a self-sustaining, day-in-and-day-out bore; a man must be at least thirty-five before he can manage that. Youth has a buoyancy, a resiliency, which makes it impossible for the young to keep to that dead-level which is the very heart and essence of the bore's craft. The spirits of youth keep bobbing up and down; a bore must be steady as a rock. The eye of youth sometimes lightens; the eye of the bore is glazed with the film of stupidity. There are gloomy bores, and agreeable bores, and eager bores and stuffy bores, but once they have set their course and determined their character, they do not change. . . . This young man, however, was in strict training to become an agreeable bore, and as he seemed naturally gifted in that respect he may achieve his aim before thirty-five, and become one of the youngest bores in Canadian history. And if he does he will be a lesson in what may be achieved by persistent effort.

JEOFFRY / Dined with some friends and admired their seven-toed cat; upon each of its forepaws it has an extra toe. Did this, I pondered, make him a better clamberer than ordinary cats? I was reminded forcibly of the cat Jeoffry, who belonged to the poet Christopher Smart, and about whom Smart wrote what I consider to be one of the most remarkable poems in the English language, praising Jeoffry's excellence as a clamberer as an evidence of the glory of God –

> For he keeps the Lord's watch in the night
>   against the adversary.
> For he counteracts the powers of darkness by
>   his electrical skin and glaring eyes.
> For he counteracts the Devil, who is death, by

> brisking about the life.
> For in his morning orisons he loves the sun and
> the sun loves him.

My friends' cat was named Sydney, but like every good cat he bore a resemblance to Smart's Jeoffry.

LILLIPUT / Some children I know were showing me a doll's house which they had been given at Christmas. It was a spacious and pleasant dwelling which, on the human scale, could not be built for less than $80,000 at present costs. I should judge that some doll of the junior executive class lived in it. Like so many doll's houses, it lacked a staircase; dolls are used to being heaved from one floor to another. It was fully, though conventionally, furnished, and over the mantel in the drawing-room was that picture "The Boyhood of Raleigh" which suggested to me that the dolls were rather old-fashioned and romantic in their tastes, in spite of the modernity of some of their furniture. I envied the father-doll the neatness of his garage; mine, which doubles as toolshed, is a sorry thing beside it. The dolls had a remarkably nice bathroom, too, quite unlike the cornery afterthought at Marchbanks Towers. I enquired whether the dolls owned or rented, and was told that they were owners; roughly I computed their land-tax, school-tax and improvements tax, and decided that these dolls were not the sort of people I would be asked to dine with, if some sudden shrinkage should whisk me into their world.

CANADIAN CAUTION / It is wrong to say that Canadians have no distinctive national characteristics; what about our national custom of Keeping Down With the Joneses? In other countries people keep up with the Joneses; they vie with one another in the acquirement of showy and prestige-giving possessions. But the crafty Canadian always wants his neighbours to think that he has less money than he really has. He underdresses, for the possession of more than two suits might suggest affluence and a desire to seem glorious in the eyes of men. His wife probably has a fur coat, but she wears it to do the shopping, and to sweep off the stoop, so that it is really just a hard-wearing overall, and not a token of wealth. He eats good food, but he likes it to be disguised, so that even the tooth-test sometimes fails to reveal how good it is. It is only when he goes on a holiday to the USA that he splurges, takes suites in hotels, gives huge tips to hirelings, and drinks pearls dissolved in wine. At home he likes the neighbours to think that he is just keeping out of jail. Surely this is a striking and unusual national attitude?

*

COMMUNIQUÉ (*delivered by a Police car, envelope stamped* OFFICIAL)

To Big Chief Marchbanks.

How, Marchbanks:

Us fellows in jail fix New Year Dance. Ball and Chain Ball, we call it. We got no women, so no dance. We got no booze, so no drink. We got no money, so no gamble. But we got peace and plenty dirty story. You want ticket? Fight cop. He give you ticket.

> Osceola Thunderbelly
> (Chief of the Crokinoles).

*

CULLED FROM THE APOPHTHEGMS
OF WIZARD MARCHBANKS

Do not be discouraged by lack of immediate success. Bernard Shaw flowered at 17, but nobody smelled him until he was 40.

Uranus

Feb. 1, 1937
Richard Dandiprat
born: father unknown

Aquarius

fixed, very watery

(January 21 to February 19)

AQUARIUS IS the sign of the Water Carrier and astrologers have long recognized that more famous people are born under this sign than under all the rest put together. The dualism of the sign explains this; the Water Carrier is always carrying water to somebody or something but whether it is hot water or cold water can rarely be determined in advance. Hot Water Aquarians are

* 174

the prophets, the great conquerors and the dictators. Cold Water Aquarians are the philosophers, the satirists and the analytic thinkers. Those born under this sign should decide as early in life as possible which group they are best fitted to join. But do not be deceived: at first glance it appears easier to pour cold water on people and things than hot water, but remember that you may have to continue this for eighty years or more – because Aquarians are long-lived. For those in whom intellect is not a strong point, hot-water is always best. A rare type of Aquarian is capable of pouring both hot and cold water – singly, both at once, or sometimes so mingled that the rare and valuable Luke-warm Aquarian emerges. The highest offices in the church, and the most prized editorial chairs await Aquarians so ambiguously gifted.

Enchantment-of-the-Month
▸✳✦✛✳✦✛✳✦✛✳✦✛✳✦✛✳✦✛✳✦✛✳✦

Your lucky colours are light blue, greeny-blue and bluey-violet. Your lucky flowers are the tulip, pansy and daffodil. Your lucky stones are the opal, sapphire, beryl and lapis-lazuli. This latter sounds better than it is, being a sort of sulphurous silicate; however, it is a very pretty blue. Wizard Marchbanks suggests that instead of wearing it, which might prove inconvenient, as it looks best in very large chunks, you bring it into the conversation casually. "Your eyes," you say to any young woman whom you wish to impress, and who does not happen to be a geologist, "have the lovely, changing, mysterious shades of lapis-lazuli." She will probably like this, as she has almost certainly never seen the stone in question and does not know that it is no more changeable in hue than the slate of a blackboard. Her apprecia-tion will make it a lucky stone for you. Similarly, a young woman may say, at the right moment, "The night sky has an almost painful beauty – like lapis-lazuli." Do not try this remark upon escorts of coarse nature, however, or third-year students of mining engineering.

Health Hints for Those Born Under Aquarius

Candour before everything: you must be on your guard against constipation. Don't ask me why. Nobody has ever died of it, and the old wives' tale about auto-intoxication (accepted as scientific fact for a few decades) has now been exploded. But there is a widespread belief that this tardy habit of body is harmful, and an astrologer is no man to fly in the face of old beliefs. Wizard Marchbanks is of the opinion that constipation of body is a trifle – a mere idiosyncrasy like double-jointedness or being able to wiggle your ears – but he warns against constipation of mind, which is a widespread and neglected illness. Costiveness of body afflicts no one but the person concerned: costiveness of mind afflicts everybody with whom the sufferer comes in contact. If he occupies a high place in the world (and the ailment is a positive recommendation in many professions) he may do more harm than a hundred men of normal mental processes can undo in a lifetime.

*

FROM MY NOTEBOOKS

FRANKNESS DEPLORED / There are too many people in the world who think that frankness is an excuse for anything: so long as a man is frank and sincere, say they, he may talk as he likes. They also cling to the stupid and mistaken notion that people like and admire frankness and respond well to it. For instance, I was standing on a street-corner today, when a man in a windbreaker approached me and said: "Lookit, I'm goin' to give you no bull; I wanta get a coupla beers; will you gimme the money?" I looked deep into his eyes, and in low, thrilling voice I said "No." . . . Now if he had given me some bull – some richly-ornamented tale of poverty, of undeserved ill-fortune, of being robbed while on some errand of mercy – anything in fact which would have revealed a spark of imagination in him, I would have given him a small sum, knowing full well that it would be spent on beer. But to ask me, flatly and baldly, for money to buy beer – ! Is that the way to appeal to a Welshman, a lover of the spoken word and the gem-encrusted lie? No, no. Let such ruffians beg beer-money from those who admire frankness. Anybody who wants a quarter from me must first produce a quarter's worth of fascinating bull.

ARS CELARE ARTIS / Chatted with a lady who once saw the Russian Imperial Ballet in the Czar's own theatre, in 1912. I asked her for a description: "Like being in Heaven," said she. I asked for more detail: "Oh, just like Heaven!" she replied. I have often observed that people who have had some experience of this kind –have seen Irving, or heard Melba, or Chaliapin – are unable to give any satisfactory account of it. They remember only that they were uplifted; they do not know why or how. Perhaps it is best that this should be so. The aim of great art is to produce this sensation of ravishment, and not to explain its methods or reveal its secrets. The chief dancer on this occasion, the lady said, was the Czar's "how do you say? – Favorita? What is favorita in English?" "Girl-friend?" suggested another guest.

The lady's face filled with distaste. "Oh no," said she, "a favorita is much diffierent. More – how do you say it – elegant." So much for girl-friends.

FOOLISH CONTEMPORANEITY / In a news vendor's today I noticed a pile of books with bright covers, which proved to be such titles as Dreiser's *Sister Carrie*, and Romains' *Jean Christophe*. Wondering idly how such long books were crammed into such a small space I picked one up and found that it was marked "abridged for the Modern Reader." Laughed out loud, and a few people stared at me, as if I were mad. But I was delighted by the shoddy flattery of that word "modern." It implied that the modern reader was a very busy fellow, who had no time to be bothered with the windy nonsense even of first-rate authors; he had to have everything boiled down for him, so that he could gulp the essence in an evening's reading. The real fact of the matter is that many modern readers are pin-headed neurotics, who have not the staying power to read a great book at full length. They must have it cut so that they can read all the bits which describe how the heroine went to bed, and with whom, and any murders which may creep into the tale. Beyond that, they can't understand and don't care. Modern reader! Pah!

*

FROM MY FILES

To Raymond Cataplasm, M.D., F.R.C.P.

Dear Dr. Cataplasm:

I am greatly worried, and I am worried because I am worried, for I read in several magazines with large circulations (which means that they must be good) that worry causes high blood pressure and ulcers, and that high blood pressure and the things which go with it kill more people than any other group of ailments. How can I stop worrying about worrying? If I could do that I could begin on the job of ceasing to worry altogether.

The notion that worry shortens the life-span is a new one to me, for my family are remarkably long-lived, and they are all master-worriers. And after they have passed the age of eighty they raise worry to the virtuoso level, worrying about things which cannot even be understood by less gifted people. But if worry is a shortener of life I must root out this ingrained ancestral habit, or I may drop off my perch at some disgracefully early age.

All the magazine advice to worriers stresses the need of relaxation. Apparently one ought to be as relaxed as possible all the time. Now when I relax completely, I fall down; I have to keep a tiny bit strung-up in order to get my work done, and to retain the respect of my colleagues. The only way for me to achieve complete relaxation is to go to bed in a darkened room. But that makes me fall asleep, and the magazine articles say that too much sleep is worse than too little. I can also relax after eating a very large meal, but over-eating is not only bad for the blood pressure, but a cause of ulcers, as well.

I am doing my best to live a healthy, relaxed, temperate, unworried life, but you doctors are making it very hard for me. In fact, you are worrying me, and you know what worry does.

Yours confusedly and miserably,
Samuel Marchbanks.

*

To Haubergeon Hydra, ESQ.

Dear Mr. Hydra:

I see that Parliament is much concerned about the quality of modern Canadianism. Apparently it is not Canadian enough – there are still big lumps of British Influence and Colonial Inferiority Complex swimming around in it. May I make a suggestion to you as Deputy Assistant Sterilizer of Canadian Patriotism?

We need bigger and better Canadian heroes. We have the raw material, but we must work on it. You know how Canada hates anything raw. We have heroes, but we have not yet blown them up to full heroic stature.

Look at what has been done in the States with Washington, Lincoln, Barbara Frietchie and others. Unpromising material to begin with. Just men and women. But by the use of gas and mirrors they have been given heroic stature. Think what that story about the Cherry Tree has done for Washington! We couldn't copy it, of course, for in Canada we still admire people who cut down trees, and could not see any particular nobility in admitting such an action. In Canada, a tree is still looked upon as a Big Weed, to be hoiked up or chopped down, or mutilated with impunity. But there are other stories which we could bend to our use, and I submit the following examples for your consideration.

SIR JOHN AND THE SPIDER

One day our Great National Hero, Sir John A. Macdonald, sat disconsolately in his lawyer's office in Kingston. Try as he might, he could not get the Canadian provinces to confederate. They simply wouldn't. As he sat, his eyes were attracted by a little spider which was trying to climb up a piece of string (or whatever that stuff is that spiders extrude so unpleasantly from their stomachs). He paid no attention, for spiders were then, as now, part of the standard furnishings of all lawyers' offices in Canada.

Up the spider climbed, and down it fell. Sir John's left eyelid twitched. Again the spider tried to climb the string, but again it fell with an arachnidal curse. And a third time it struggled up the string, and immediately set to work to gobble up a juicy fly.

Sir John was now fully awake. "By George!" he cried (referring to George Brown of the Toronto *Globe*, and thus uttering a terrible Conservative curse) "shall yonder foolish insect put me to shame? I too shall strive, and strive again, until there is a Federal Government in Canada, gobbling up the richest flies the land affords!" And hastily taking a drink of soda water (of which he was inordinately fond) he rushed out and confederated Canada in a twinkling.

Moral: Never sweep your office.

LAURIER AND THE TEAKETTLE

One day Sir Wilfrid Laurier sat by the hearth in his parents' home, musing and pondering in French (though being completely bilingual, he could just as easily have done it in English). Beside him, on the hob, the kettle bubbled. "Etre, ou non être?" mused Sir Wilfrid; "c'est la question." (This splendid line was later incorporated into the film of *Hamlet*, but it lost a great deal in translation). "Blubbety-blub!" mused the kettle, in kettle-language. "Qu'est-ce que c'est que vous avez dit?" asked Sir Wilfrid. "Bloop!" said the kettle.

In that instant Sir Wilfrid conceived the whole theory of the steam-engine, and would have built a railway to the Yukon if the Senate had not vetoed the idea.

Moral: The Senate should be reformed so as to consist entirely of the Cabinet.

LAURA'S JEWELS

The constant companions of the great and good Laura Secord were her cows. Indeed, it was a cow which overheard the American officers planning their wicked attack upon Colonel Fitzgibbon's troops, and warned Laura. The story that she herself listened at the keyhole is a vicious canard. Being immovably upright, she could not stoop to a keyhole.

One day she was entertaining a purse-proud friend who boasted immoderately of her riches and her articles of personal adornment. "And will you not show me your jewels, Mrs. Secord?" said she.

Smiling enigmatically Laura called her cows to her. She put her arms around each brown neck, drawing the wet noses close to her own. "These are my jewels," said she, with well-nigh unbearable simplicity.

Moral: The cream of the cream can get along without diamonds, even of the first water.

There you have it Mr. Hydra. Fill our children up with that sort of thing, and in no time their patriotism will have surpassed even our most unreasonable expectations.

Yours for an aggressively Canadian Canada,
    Samuel Marchbanks.

*

To Samuel Marchbanks, ESQ.

Honoured Sir:
    On behalf of our client, Mr. Richard Dandiprat, we write to ask if it would not be possible to settle your difference with him in some amicable way which does not involve court procedure. Lawsuits among neighbours are to be avoided whenever possible, as we are sure you will agree. We learn to our amazement and chagrin that Mr. Dandiprat has written letters to you in which he virtually confesses that it was he who imprisoned a skunk in your car while you were abroad. This was indiscreet, but Mr. Dandiprat is a man of lovable and open nature and concealment is distasteful to him.
    We venture to suggest that if you care to pay some small sum – we suggest $2,500 – to Mr. Dandiprat as recompense for all the mental distress which your threatened lawsuit has cost him, the matter can be closed with good will on both sides.

Yours in a spirit of neighbourly forgiveness,
    Jasper Raven
    (for Raven and Craven, Solicitors).

*

To Raven and Craven.

Sirs:
    So, you are crawling, are you? Whining for mercy, eh? No, no, gentlemen, I intend to roast your client, Dandiprat, before the fire of enraged public opinion. To your roost, Raven! To your lair, Craven, lest you perish with Dandiprat in the whirlwind of my wrath!

Yours in triumph,
    Samuel Marchbanks.

*

To Samuel Marchbanks, ESQ.

Honoured, Esteemed – nay, Beloved Sir:

Oh, Mr. Marchbanks, what a bitter tale I have to tell! Last Autumn, with Hallowe'en approaching, we sent two or three of our secretarial staff into the cellar to bring up the base-burner which heats our office in the Winter months. Hallowe'en is, as you know, a festival dear to the hearts of lawyers, and Mr. Jabez Mouseman loves to see the flames flickering behind the little mica windows in the stove when the great day dawns. The girls got the stove into the office, and with some difficulty they set it up, and fitted the stovepipes into the wall. But when it came time to light the fire, ah, then –. You know how impatient the old are, Mr. Marchbanks. My dear father, Mr. Jabez Mouseman, seized what he imagined to be some valueless material from a filing cabinet, and lit the fire. Unlucky fate guided his hand. It was your file, and all the evidence, so carefully piled up, and all the incriminating letters from Dandiprat are gone.

But the law is not without resource, sir. We shall rewrite all the documents, from memory, as soon as possible. We shall even provide facsimiles of the signatures. In the end the evidence will be better than ever. But for a law-term or two we shall be wise to allow the case to drift along without too much activity.

Yours in sorrow,
    Mordecai Mouseman
      (for Mouseman, Mouseman and Forcemeat).

P.S.: The cost of restoring the evidence will add considerably to your legal expenditures, but Let Right Be Done is the motto of our firm.

✳

To the Rev. Simon Goaste, B.D.

Dear Pastor Goaste:

In the course of your theological studies, did you ever run across anything which would give you a clue to the exact temperature of Hell? I find that among my friends there is a widespread notion that Hell will be hot. My own conviction is that it will be cold.

Frankly, if I had the management of Hell I should arrange for it to be a place where everybody had to sit on kitchen chairs, in a bad light, at a temperature of about 45 degrees Fahrenheit, reading the *Canada Gazette*. A few aeons of that would show sinners what was what.

Yours reflectively,
    Samuel Marchbanks.

✳

To Samuel Marchbanks, ESQ.

Dear Mr. Marchbanks:

Could you, offhand, name the most wronged group of men in Canada today? No, of course you couldn't, but I, as Perpetual President of the Indignant Females (Canadian Division) will name it for you. Policemen!

Almost every word which is applied to the police in everyday life is a term of derision. Take "flatfoot" for instance. It is a patent misnomer. The Indignant Females have taken plaster impressions of the feet of over two thousand Canadian police, and a majority of them have feet which are slightly rounded on the sole; the completely flat foot, shaped like a brick, was found in little more than nine hundred cases. Nor is it true that policemen have unusually big feet; our investigations reveal that postmen have bigger feet, and that policemen compare favourably with bill collectors in this respect.

Yours indignantly,
(Mrs.) Kedijah Scissorbill.

＊

To Amyas Pilgarlic, ESQ.

Dear Pil:

A man I know has been boasting in the public prints recently about the difficulties which he has encountered in opening oysters. I can only conclude that he has never acquired this knack. The way to open an oyster is to insert a chisel, or perhaps a small poker, into the imperceptible cranny at the sharp end of the oyster, and heave. With not much more trouble than would be found in opening the main vault of the Bank of England, the upper shell will stir a little, and it is at this point that your assistants should push heavy wooden wedges (oak, for choice) between the shells. Then blow cigarette smoke into the cracks and the oyster will sneeze, neatly blowing its top. No trick at all, once you are used to it, and in this way half a dozen oysters may be opened in an hour.

Lincoln said that he who cuts his own wood warms himself twice. Marchbanks says that he who opens his own oysters gives himself an appetite.

Did you know, by the way, that the great singer Adelina Patti (1843-1919) loved oysters, and used to sing so exquisitely after eating them that she would cause the most torpid audience to leap to its feet? This ability on her part suggested the name for that elegant confection, the Hoister Patti.

Yours,
Sam.

＊

To Chambers Fribble, ESQ.

Learned Fribble:

I have been reading a good deal of Canadian Poetry lately, and it has disturbed me. But last Sunday I attempted to go for a country walk, and by the time I had reached home again I knew what was wrong with Canadian Poetry.

Canadian poets are not allowed to come into contact with Nature. The great English poets have, in most cases, refreshed themselves continually by spells of country life, or by excursions into the country. Canadian poets cannot do this. I walked about two miles in the country and although I did not count them I estimated that roughly 300 cars passed me in that time. I had no time for Nature; I was perpetually on the jump. So I decided to walk across country. A farmer chased me, and told me not to tramp on his Fall wheat, which I was not doing. However, I left his land and struck into the bush. This was a mistake, for a big dog came and pointed his nose at me, and did his best to look like a bronze dog on a book-end. Soon two men with guns came crashing through the undergrowth, and seemed astonished when they saw me. "Say, what's that bird doing here?" cried one, and I knew at once that they had mistaken me for a partridge. But as they seemed about to blast my tailfeathers off I had the presence of mind to shout "I'm a game-warden!" and they made off as fast as their legs would carry them. The dog was still pointing, and as stiff as a mackerel, so they snatched it up in one piece and bore it away with them.

That is what Nature means in Canada. Cars, grouchy landowners, people with guns. No wonder our poetry is of nervous, urban, over-bred elegance.

Yours for a less cluttered countryside,
Samuel Marchbanks.

*

MUSINGS AT EVENTIDE

THE RULING PASSION / I was introduced to a lady this evening who said, "Well, and do you still do any writing on the side?" I simpered and said, "Oh, a little, you know," for I was so thunderstruck that I could not collect my wits in time to make a proper rejoinder. But I made a speech to her in my head, afterward, which ran thus: "Woman, for almost all of my adult life I have lived by the pen, with some assistance from the typewriter and the printing press. I do not write 'on the side' as you insultingly suggest. I write morning, noon and night. When I am not actually engaged in the physical act of writing I am thinking about writing – my own and other people's. Writing is my business and my pleasure, my cross and my salvation, my joy and my sorrow." But it would have been foolish to say this aloud. There are many millions of people who think that writing, and painting, and music are things which their practitioners pick up in an idle hour; they have no conception of the demands which these apparently trivial pastimes make upon those who are committed to them. Such people live in a world which is as strange to me as the Mountains of the Moon.

BLUE DANUBE / Concert-going, which most people look upon as pleasure, is part of my work, and it is surprising how one's pleasure in a concert is dulled when one knows it will be necessary to write something about it. . . . The singer sang several songs in praise of the gaiety of Vienna. Was Vienna ever really so gay as we are asked to believe? I can find no evidence of it. Sigmund Freud lived in Vienna during its supposedly gayest period, and had a pretty solemn time among the foot-fetichists and undinists on the beautiful Blue Danube. Stefan Zweig in his autobiography tells us that the gay Viennese ate so much whipped cream and almond paste that they were all fat at thirty, and wheezed as they waltzed. The leading romance of the period was the Emperor's very dull and proper affair with Kathi Schratt. I have even heard it suggested that those parties at Sacher's were rather quiet. There is plenty of evidence that Vienna in its heyday was about as gay as Calgary, but it was luckier in having a handful of really good song-writers.

POSTURE PROBLEM / I observe with no enthusiasm it is National Posture Week in the USA; thank Heaven this heathen festival is not being observed in Canada. When I was young we were taught that the only proper posture for the boy was that of a sentry at attention – eyes glazed, chest bursting, shoulders under the ears, toes curled and chin digging into the Adam's apple. Later this position was somewhat relaxed, and it was admitted that it was sometimes permissible to touch the heels to the ground. Recently a scientist who had done a lot of work with monkeys has said that a relaxed posture, leaning forward and ambling like a gorilla, is the best and most natural for man. So confused am I by these changes that I have developed my own posture, which has two phases – standing up and lying down. I cannot sit. I lie in chairs on the back of my neck, allowing gravity to drag my vital organs toward the floor. When I stand, I lose height at the rate of about two inches every hour. In the morning, when I am thoroughly uncoiled, I am six feet tall; if my day involves much standing, I am five feet tall by lunchtime, four feet six inches by dinner, and go to bed a midget. Posture is a word I prefer not to use in connection with myself.

*

FROM MY ARCHIVES

To Samuel Marchbanks, ESQ.

Dear Mr. Marchbanks:

I have just finished reading a book by the eminent child-psychologist, Dr. Blutwurst Susskind, in which he makes it clear that what children want more than anything in the world is parental love. It is this desire, he says, which makes children ask questions at inconvenient times, wake their parents up early in the morning, kick them on the shins, and in general behave in a way which thoughtless parents call "making a nuisance of themselves." Dr. Susskind says that an eager child should never be rebuffed. The parents should say: "I love you dearly, but I haven't time to attend to you now," or something of the sort.

Now I have a scheme which I would like you, as an internationally-known lover of children, to assist me in popularizing. It is based upon the old system of Sunday School cards which you will remember: a child got a small card for each visit to S.S.; when it had ten small cards it could exchange them for a large card; when it had ten large cards it could get a Bible. Now my idea is that a parent should have a stock of cards saying: "Love you dearly; busy now," which it could hand to the child which interrupted at an inconvenient moment. Ten such cards could be exchanged for a large card saying: "Dote upon you madly, go away." Ten of these large cards could be exchanged for a visit to the circus, a picnic, a soda-guzzle or some similar treat.

The cards, I feel, could most effectively be sold through the Home and School Clubs; the whole scheme could be financed for a beggarly $100,000 and it is for this laughable sum that I confidently turn to you.

Yours with complete confidence,
Minerva Hawser.

*

To Miss Minerva Hawser.

Dear Miss Hawser:

How lucky that your letter reached me when it did! I was just about to write to you about a scheme of my own for the improvement of the lot of children, which is a notoriously hard one in our age. It has been my observation that many children suffer real hardship because they want to see all (not just a few) TV programs, but they are of such a restless bodily composition that there are times when they simply have to get up from their seats and run about. This means, of course, that they lose many desirable half-hours of prime viewing-time.

I have devised a small battery TV which any child can wear concealed in its hat; electric wires running down from the hat into the child's shoes keep the battery constantly charged by the energy which the child generates as it runs, operating a tiny portable set. Thus the child may play and teleview at the same time, without missing a thing.

As it happens I also need $100,000 to launch this scheme, and had decided to turn to you for it. We can both go on with our work, therefore, without even troubling to exchange cheques.

With thanks for your invaluable help,
Samuel Marchbanks.

＊

To Samuel Marchbanks, ESQ.

Dear Sam:
I was reading a new book about the eighteenth century a few days ago, and came upon some references to Dr. Samuel Johnson and his cat Hodge; the author remarked that however out of temper the great Doctor might be, the appearance of Hodge was enough to put him in a good humour. I send you, therefore, the following poem, which I have called *Remarkable Power of a Cat to Soothe a Raging Philosopher*:

Dr. Johnson's cat Hodge
Was up to every feline dodge:
When the Doctor shouted "Sir!"
Hodge would disarmingly interject "Purr."

Rather good, don't you think?
Pilgarlic.

＊

To Chandos Fribble, ESQ.

Learned Fribble:
Yesterday a picture in a magazine for women, called *Glamour*, was drawn to my attention; it showed a reasonably toothsome young woman wearing spectacles, engaged in reading a large leather-bound book; with one hand she was thoughtfully scratching her head. Underneath the picture was advice, addressed to women in general, to curl up with a good book.

This is an expression which I am at a loss to understand. I

read a good many books myself, but I never feel disposed to curl up while doing so. Now and then in the course of my duties as a book-reviewer I read a book which causes me to curl, slightly, but not with pleasure; I uncurl at once and write something nasty about the books. Why are women such curlers, in their literary moods?

I may say, in passing, that I would never dream of lending a book to a woman who was a head-scratcher. Human hair and dandruff are nasty things to find between the pages of a book. I once knew a man who used his pipe as a bookmark. At least women are free from that disgusting trick.

But to return to our curling; have you ever tried to curl up with a book? It brings about cramp; it makes you read sideways, which is bad for the eyes; persisted in, it gives you not only curvature of the spine, but curvature of the brain, and a low literary taste.

You have heard people say of somebody that he has a wrong slant on things. He got it by curling up with the wrong books, and reading them sideways.

Yours, from my armchair,
Samuel Marchbanks.

*

To Waghorn Wittol, ESQ.

My good Wittol:

I am flattered that you should appeal to me so often for advice, but really I cannot suggest any means by which you may regain Mrs. Wittol's wandering affections. At least, nothing which I think will work.

However, if you are interested in a scheme which probably won't work, may I suggest that you have recourse to the Language of the Eyes? I was reading about it the other day in a novel by Ouida, an authoress who is unaccountably neglected these days. The passage ran thus: "Olga Brancka looked at him with some malice and more admiration; she was very pretty that night, blazing with diamonds and with her beautifully shaped person as bare as court etiquette would allow; there was a butterfly, big as the great Emperor moth, between her breasts, making their whiteness look like snow. The glance was not lost upon him; in the Language of Eyes it seemed to say, 'This might be yours.'" See – he could have had that moth for the asking.

As it happens, I am one of the few great masters of the Language of Eyes living today. I practise it at my dentist's. When I lower my lids to half-mast it means "You are brutal." When I push them out of their sockets like ping-pong balls it means "This is unbearable." When I cause them to roll around the edges of their sockets, like billiard balls wondering whether or not to fall into the pocket, it means "I am about to faint." When I cross and uncross them, with an audible clicking, it means "Pain has bereft me of reason." You say that it is useless to talk to Mrs. Wittol; why don't you try the Language of Eyes? Ouida and I both recommend it.

Yours in hope (but not high hope),

Samuel Marchbanks.

*

To Chandos Fribble, ESQ.

Worthy Fribble:

It is indeed good news that you intend to prepare a book on the Rights of Women in Canada. I shall await the appearance of the Fribble Report with keen expectation. Is it true that the French translation is to be called, with greater frankness, *L'Amour au Canada*?

Meanwhile, let me report for you a curious conversation which I heard the other night, when I attended an entertainment where a great many adolescents were present. Behind me sat a boy and a girl, both about fifteen.

BOY: (Laughing at one of his own jokes) "G'wan, cut out that laffin.'"

GIRL: "Gee, I can't. You got me laffin' so's I can't stop."

BOY: (delighted) "Cut it out, I tell yuh. Everybody's lookin' at yuh."

GIRL: (trying to stifle mirth) "Fsssst! Splut! Eeeeeeeek!"

BOY: (transported) "Cut it out! Cut it out!"

GIRL: "Gee I can't! Not if you're gonna say funny things like that!"

BOY: "Juh want me to take yuh out in the hall and slap yuh around? That'll stopyuh!"

GIRL: (ecstatic at the idea) "Aw, yer killin' me! Fsssst!"

Here, I think we have a fairly typical pattern of Canadian sexual behaviour. The male, having subdued the female by his superior intellectual power, dominates and even threatens her. This produces in her a mounting physical and psychological pleasure, like the rising of steam in a boiler. This psychological pressure causes her to kick the back of my seat in an irregular rhythm, similar to the mating-dance of the Whooping Crane. It is this sort of thing that makes Canada the Amorist's paradise it is.

I shall inform you of any other interesting manifestations of the biological urge which may come under my eye.

Scientifically yours,

Marchbanks.

To Dionysus Fishorn, ESQ.

Dear Mr. Fishorn:

No, I will not support your application for a Canada Council grant to enable you to write your novel. I know nothing about you, but I know a good deal about novels, and you are on the wrong track.

You say you want money to be "free of care" for a year, so that you can "create," and you speak of going to Mexico, to live cheaply and avoid distraction. Fishorn, I fear that your fictional abilities have spilled over from your work into your life. You see yourself in some lovely, unspoiled part of Mexico, where you will stroll out of your study onto the patio after a day's "creation," to gaze at the sunset and get into the cheap booze; your wife will admire you extravagantly and marvel that you ever condescended to marry such a workaday person as herself; the villagers will speak of you with awe as El Escritor, and will pump your beautiful servant Ramona for news of your wondrous doings; you will go down into the very depths of Hell in your creative frenzies, but you will emerge, scorched and ennobled, in time for publication, translation into all known languages, and the Nobel Prize.

Ah, Fishorn, would that it were so! But take the advice of an old hand: you won't write any better in Mexico than in Tin Cup, B.C., and unless you are wafted into a small, specially favoured group of the insane, you will never be free from care. So get to work, toiling in the bank or wherever it is by day, and serving the Triple Goddess at night and on weekends. Art is long, and grants are but yearly, so forget about them. A writer should not take handouts from anybody, even his country.

Benevolently but uncompromisingly,
Samuel Marchbanks.

*

OBITER DICTA

DREAM MAIDENS / Saw a motor-bicycle parked in the street today, and on its wind-screen were several alluring pictures of girls, one of whom wore what appeared to be a scanty outfit of leopardskin underwear; she stretched her arms above her head (presumably in order to give greater freedom to her considerable bosom) and carried a banner upon which was written "If you don't see what you want, ask for it." As I looked, the owner came out of a house, mounted the machine, kicked it fiercely in the slats several times, and at last goaded it into action. He was a smallish, mousey fellow with rimless glasses, and did not look to me as though his acquaintance included any girls who wore leopard next their skins. And it has been my usual experience that all those wildly improbable girls who exist only in the minds of artists appeal chiefly to young men who either know no girls at all, or know only girls of a mousiness equal to their own. Pin-up girls are dreams, and dreams unlikely to come true. And a good thing, perhaps, for what would the average young man do with a girl who never put on her clothes and whose bosom accounted for one-third of her total weight?

FEATHERED FUTURITY / I see by the paper that Rhythmic Arithmetic has been abandoned in the schools. I never understood what it was, though much time was wasted by adult educators explaining it to me, and I never met a child who could explain it. But I have long recognized that I have no mathematical facility whatever. Plato, who was a brainy fellow, said that "innocent, light-minded men who know no mathematics will become birds after death"; I rather look forward to being a bird, and taking a bird's revenge on all my enemies. Plato also thought that men who had no philosophy would become animals after death; really stupid people would continue their existence as fish; "cowardly and unrighteous men," he asserted, would find that in the next world they had been turned into women. Plato had a poor opinion of women, which would make life difficult for him if he were born again in this century; he also thought little of the professional educators of his day, an attitude which would make it utterly impossible for him to get a certificate to teach in a one-room country school in Twentieth Century Canada.

WORD OF HORROR / Was talking to a musical person who informed me that a celebrated pianist would "concertize" in Toronto next month. This remark nearly caused me to swallow my pipe, for though I have seen the vile word "concertize" in print for several years this was the first time I had ever heard anyone use it in conversation. I was taken aback as if my hostess had said, "Won't you climax your meal with another cup of coffee?" Such words fill me with an urge to seize the person who uses them in a commando grip and twist him (more often the offender is a she) until I have broken every bone. Then their broken-boned walking would be appropriate to their broken-boned speech. O Mighty Music! Did David concertize before Saul, or Bach before Frederick the Great? Did Beethoven concertize? (In the time, of course, when they were not composerizing.) No, apes and dung-beetles, they PLAYED!

SUPER-BOY / To a concert given by a group of choir boys from Vienna. It was an admirable evening's entertainment, which was more than I had expected for I am not an enthusiastic admirer of the Human Boy. In my reckoning boys range from Good Boys – that is, boys who can pass the Towers without upsetting garbage cans and throwing rubbish on the lawn – to the lowest dregs of humanity, depraved slubberdegullions who do the above things, and worse. But these Viennese boys were quite unusual in several respects; they were clean; they were well-behaved; their hair was brushed; they looked as though they might be trusted with whole rows of garbage cans. . . . This was the first time I have ever heard choir boys who were not trained in the English tradition of fruity hooting; an English choirboy sounds like a lovesick owl, and although it is a pretty sound it moves me to a gentle melancholy – a kind of Sunday-night-and-another-week's-work-starts-tomorrow feeling. . . . Sometimes people say to me: Were you never a boy yourself, Mr. Marchbanks? Answer: Yes, for several years I was a noble, dutiful, clean, respectful Super-Boy.

*

COMMUNIQUÉ (*dropped at my door by an escaped prisoner*)

To Big Chief Marchbanks.

How, Marchbanks:

You got any old magazines, Marchbanks? Magazines in jail awful. Sent here after long hard life in dentist office. All girl pictures got bustles. Educated fellow in jail read story out loud other day. Good story about detective. Name Sherlock Holmes. Magazine say this first story about him ever. But last page gone. Doctor leave magazine bundle here yesterday. Magazine all about how have babies. We know that already. Anyway that squaw work. You got magazines tell us what we don't know?

Osceola Thunderbelly
(Chief of the Crokinoles).

*

CULLED FROM THE APOPHTHEGMS OF WIZARD MARCHBANKS

Be most alert when most victorious, for though you may not hit your adversary when he is down, it is considered plucky in him to kick *you*.

191 *

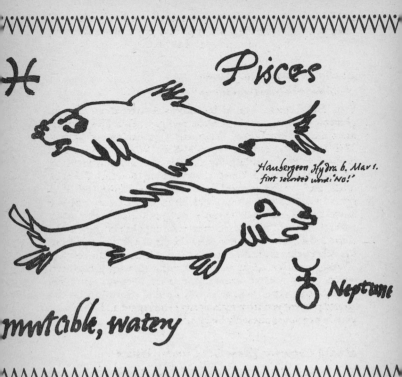

Pisces

Haubergeon Hydra b. Mar 1.
first recorded word: 'No!'

Neptune

mutable, watery

(February 20 to March 21)

PISCES IS the sign of the Crossed Fish. As in the case of Capricorn,
Wizard Marchbanks advises you to make the best of this, and in
particular to take fullest advantage of the cool temperament and
the calmly reflective eye with which nature has endowed you.
Always remember that the Crossed Fish are moving in two
directions and one of them is inevitably the opposite direction
from whatever trouble may be brewing. Because you are elusive
and slow to take a bait you may miss some of the spectacular
fun of life, but you will find your amusement in observing
what happens to those born under more impetuous signs. It is
especially necessary for the Pisces-born to be careful in marriage
and business associations, for any prolonged association with a
Hot Water Aquarian will prove disturbing if not downright
fatal. The Virgo- and Cancer-born should be more in your line,

and in the professional world accountancy, corporation law and other pursuits which are in the world but not of it should prove most congenial to you.

Enchantment-of-the-Month

>★>☯★>☯★>☯★>☯★>☯★>☯★>☯

Your lucky colours – or to be more scientific about it, your planetary colours – are blue, violet and grey. Your lucky flowers are a miserable collection – mignonette, jessamine and yarrow. This last is the familiar weed Milfoil; Wizard Marchbanks declines to be drawn into any discussion of what distinguishes a flower from a weed. Your lucky stones are the pearl, the chrysolite, and – rather curiously – "all unpolished blue and black gems." Chrysolite is a silicate of magnesia and iron which is found in lava and is not very interesting; pearls are much better. Perhaps it would be wiser to wear your unpolished gems under your clothes; it is one of the painful facts of life that gems look like other pebbles until they are cut and polished, and a necklace of dingy pebbles might win you a reputation for eccentricity which you would be unable to support. People born under Pisces are supposed to have a lively sense of the ridiculous; this should prevent you from making any extravagant and unsuitable parade of your supposedly lucky adornments.

Health Hints for Those Born Under Pisces

Your weak spot is your chest, and you must be on guard against colds. It is also asserted that people born under this sign are more susceptible to liquor than others, and if this is true, it is unlucky indeed, for how can you keep colds at bay without the most popular of all medicines for cold prevention, cold treatment, and convalescent encouragement? However, medical science has recently come to the aid of astrology by asserting that onions, and garlic in particular, are prophylactics against colds. Therefore, when you go to a cocktail party, load up on the pickled onions, and leave the drinks alone. Accept a martini, but when you have eaten the onion, pour the drink into a vase of flowers. It is not true that onions give you an offensive breath. People who have eaten onions may have a bad breath the next day, but the odour of fresh onion is rather agreeable than otherwise. Your plan, clearly, is to eat onions every day, and in bad weather wear a little bunch of garlic tied around your neck. Disguise it, if you like, with some blossoms of yarrow.

*

HABILOGRAPHY / For some time several newspapers that I read have been publishing hokum by graphologists, who profess to estimate character by handwriting. It is not to be compared with my own, recently-developed study of Habilography, or the Reading of Character by Clothing. I can tell volumes about a man by the ties he wears, and I place women by their shoes. The number, and nature, of the pens and pencils a man carries in his waistcoat pocket affords deep insight into his character, and a woman who wears junk jewellery combined with genuine fine stones lays bare her soul to my searching eye. What can a woman conceal from the trained Habilographer, as he mentally estimates the variations of her hemlines? And socks, those windows of thé soul, usually tell me more about a man than I really want to know. What is more truly characteristic of a human being than the draperies he sees fit to assume, the ornaments he chooses, and the way in which he has assembled the junk which conceals four-fifths of his person? Graphology – bah! Habilography – aha!

THE PAST REARRANGED / I was looking at some records today, belonging to a friend who collects oddities for the gramophone, and was interested in a series called *Immortal Voices and History Making Events*. It was an odd jumble, but I found a record of Sarah Bernhardt reciting a Prayer for Our Enemies, and put it on. Amid the rustling and scratching inseparable from old recordings there was barely audible a passionate, female voice, speaking – or to be exact, howling – in French. In the descriptive note which went with the thing Sarah Bernhardt was described as "a great lady of the American stage," and thus France was robbed of one of its glories. The US and the USSR between them are dividing not only the earth, but the past thereof.

ORGY / To a movie called *Faust and the Devil*, made in Italy, which I enjoyed greatly, and particularly an Orgy scene, where Faust made genteel and ineffective plays for several girls in filmy frocks. The Devil, meanwhile, sat at a table loaded with goodies, but ate nothing save a few grapes. Watching his weight, I suppose. Have not seen an Orgy in a movie since the days of the silent film; they often had Orgies, and they always took the form of a light meal, eaten in the company of jolly girls in peek-a-boo nighties. I have never been at an Orgy, though I suppose my garbage this morning filled the neighbourhood with dark suspicion.

LIFE AND ART / To Ottawa to attend a performance of a play by my old friend Apollo Fishorn, the Canadian playwright. Fishorn got on the train at Smith's Falls, with a live hen in a net, and a basket of fresh eggs, which he said he was taking to the actors, who appreciate these little comforts from the farm. He also had a carpet bag with a bad catch, which kept falling open and revealing the sorriest pair of pyjamas I have ever seen. . . . . I liked the play, but joining a party of knowledgeable persons in the lobby at one of the intervals, I learned that there was too much talk in it, and not enough action. Now this puzzles me. There are only a very few kinds of action which can be shown on the stage. Love is a great theme of playwrights, but if they try to develop it as action rather than as talk, the censor cracks down. Murder is good, but if you murder more than one person an act, people think you are trying to be Shakespeare, and complain. I mentioned this criticism to Fishorn, and he sighed, and said: "Yes, but life is 99 per cent talk. Look at the people who want more action in my play; what are they doing? Talking! What are you doing? Talking!" And sure enough when I caught sight of myself in a mirror, he was right.

BUILT-IN LSD / The charm of LSD, I gather from some excitable pieces for and against that have been in the papers, is that it enables the user to see deeper into inanimate things, to perceive colours more splendidly and sounds more ravishingly, than most people. It dawns upon me that it gives something of the perception of an artist – specifically a poet; indeed, it brings back something of the clean vision of childhood. I can recall, at a very early age, standing transfixed before a peony, feeling myself drawn into its gorgeous colour; I know I was very young at the time, for the peony and I were about the same height. But the important thing is that I can still do this, with sight and sound, when I choose, so it is very easy for me to go on a trip – which I believe is the expression now for this sort of experience. But one does not always enjoy it. "If a monkey looks into a mirror, no apostle will look out," says Lichtenberg, one of my favourite philosophers. We all have a good deal of monkey in us, and when he is uppermost we should be very careful about seeking extensions of experience.

DOGS ON THE UP-AND-UP / For years people have belaboured me about what they consider to be my disrelish for dogs; not only do they love dogs – I must love them too. But recently a philosopher friend (well, as much a friend as any real philosopher ever permits himself to be, for fear of accidents) took up the fight. "Dogs relate us to the chthonic realm," said he, "and without some measure of chthonicity you are an imperfect human being." He thought to bamboozle me with his fancy Greek word, but I already knew it, and what is more, I pronounce the initial "ch" which is more than he could do because he always has catarrh. It just means "of the lower world," and the lower world is much in fashion these days. But I know dogs. They are aware that they belong to a lower world, and are trying to improve themselves by begging upper-world food, lolling in upper-world chairs, and snuffling wetly at upper-world ankles (from which they proceed upward until outraged modesty demands that I give them a kick in the slats). Dogs are trying to take over, and I know it. Not that a dogocracy could be much worse than what we have now.

BLESS YOU! / Since childhood's happy hour I have been the possessor of a particularly loud sneeze. It is not the loudest in the world; an Irishman I have known for many years has a supersneeze which he heralds with a plaintive cry, somewhat like that of an epileptic just before a seizure, and beside him I am but a child in sternutation. But I am a pretty good sneezer, and kindly people say "God bless you" in awed voices, after they have crawled from under the tables where they have taken shelter. This custom of blessing a sneezer is said to have originated with Saint Gregory the Great, though the Romans said "Absit Omen," which is as near as a Roman ever got to blessing anybody. My Jewish friends, of course, say "Gesundheit" and one of them explained to me that it is an old Jewish belief, traceable to the *Cabbala*, that when a man sneezes his soul flies out of his mouth for an instant (presumably on an elastic) and in that fateful twinkling a demon may rush into his body, cut the elastic, and take charge. I know a good many people whose general hatefulness, contrariety and all-round objectionableness may well be the result of a sneeze during which the blessing was forgotten.

*

FROM MY FILES

To Apollo Fishorn, ESQ.

Dear Mr. Fishorn:

I am ashamed that a young Canadian playwright such as yourself should write to me complaining that he cannot think of a theme for a major work.

Out of pity for you, I suggest the following: the steps by which the barbarous mediaeval treatment of insane persons was supplanted by our modern comparatively humane methods.

That would make a fine chronicle play. And don't forget that the Quakers were the first people to establish a hospital in which the insane were treated as human beings with personal preferences and rights. It is a matter of history that Quakers spent many hours finding out from their patients what they liked to eat, instead of giving them dirty skilly in dippers. And there is one of your best scenes, roughly like this:

SCENE: a cell in a Quaker hospital. Mad Bess is happily banging her head against the wall. Enter a Quaker.

QUAKE: Peace be upon you, woman. Prithee give over. Thee will injure thee's brainpan.

MAD B: Yahoo! Cockyolly, cockyolly!

QUAKE: Tell me, prithee, dost thee like marmalade or jam on thee's breakfast toast?

MAD B: They say the owl was a baker's daughter.

QUAKE: Very like, dear sister. But speaking of breakfast toast –

MAD B: Come, my coach. Good night, ladies, good night.

QUAKE: It may be as thee says. But in the morning, dost thee like jam or marmalade on thee's breakfast toast?

(Enter Elizabeth Fry, the great Quaker humanitarian)

E. FRY: How fares the work, brother?

QUAKE: But tardily, sister. This dear sister here cannot say whether she wants jam or marmalade on her breakfast toast.

E. FRY: Come sister, I am Elizabeth Fry. Tell me what thee wants on thee's toast.

MAD B: Oh, so you're one of the Frys, are you? Then bring me a great big delicious, steaming, vitamin-packed cup of Cadbury's breakfast cocoa!

(Confusion; Elizabeth Fry and Quaker look pained, and Mad Bess strikes the wall again with her head; the wall breaks through; she escapes.)

There; you see how impressive it could be? Shame on you for despairing.

S. Marchbanks.

*

To Genghis Marchbanks, ESQ.

Dear Cousin Genghis:

I am laid low with a cold on my chest which I have been treating with medicated steam. How do you suppose the notion took hold of the gullible public that steam was good for such afflictions? For three days I have lived in an atmosphere like that of a Turkish bath, and I think I am worse, if anything. I have a roaring cough, and pains in my back and legs as though dozens of malignant gnomes were prodding me with old-fashioned bone hairpins. Other gnomes are busy among my tripes with knitting needles.

Steam has been my watchword in such afflictions since I was a boy. I well recall that when I lived in England a friend of mine burst into my room one day as I sat with a towel over my head inhaling the balsam fumes from a fragrant jug; he crept away on tiptoe, and told me afterward that he thought I was at some sort of special worship – a Canadian Day of Atonement – or perhaps weeping uncontrollably into the jug. But I have never found steam of much use. My face takes on a swollen, boiled look, and that is all. Still, steam is as good for a cold as anything else the medical profession has dreamed up.

Yours from the fog,
Samuel.

*

To Mervyn Noseigh, M.A.

Dear Mr. Noseigh:

No no; I am not in the least offended by your letter asking about my sex life. I fully realize that no study of an author, living or dead, is of any value without this sort of saucy exploration. And my disenchantment has undoubtedly had more effect on literature than anything since Henry James had his mysterious misadventure.

Like every Canadian of my generation, I picked up my knowledge of Sex in the gutter. I well remember the day I did so. There it was, a torn scrap of print, fluttering on the very edge of a manhole. I picked it up, and studied it with care. So far as I could make out, much of it was in foreign languages – squiggly scripts that meant nothing to me; but there was a little left of the English section, and from it I discerned that headaches, a furred tongue, and occasional spots before the eyes were signs of – the fragment was torn at that point, but it was obviously Sex.

From that time forward I made discreet enquiries of every attractive girl I met about her headaches; they never had any. Once I reached a point of intimacy where I was able to ask a marvellous girl to show me her tongue; it was as clean as could be, so obviously I had been misled about her feelings for me, and broke off the affair with a heavy heart.

Years later I discovered that what I had found in the gutter was part of the literature that comes wrapped around bottles of Eno's Fruit Salts.

Such are the tragedies that maim the lives of millions.

Yours in total disillusion,
Samuel Marchbanks.

*

To Waghorn Wittol, ESQ.

Dear Mr. Wittol:

It was a pleasure to encounter you at the theatre, but where was Mrs. Wittol? I thought I saw her with another gentleman, but very likely I was mistaken. I was much impressed by the melodrama in which a man shared with his wife the secret of a murder, and in which his wife contrived his death by a clever device. But you know, Wittol, I think that there is an even more exciting melodrama to be written about married life. What about a play in which a man and his wife, discovering that they are boring each other, set out on a race as to which can bore the other to death first?

Think of the scenes which such a drama could contain! The great scene in which the wife tells her husband the plot of a movie she has seen. He falls asleep, coma seems about to supervene until, with a tremendous effort, he rouses himself and retorts with a description of his bridge game at the club, recalling each hand in detail; she tumbles forward in her chair, and is seen to reach for the cyanide bottle. But no! She still has some fight left in her, and begins to read a letter from her mother, who is shuffle-board champion of St. Petersburg, Fla. You see the plan? A tournament of boredom! Hollywood would jump at it, but I think the Little Theatres ought to have it first.

My regards to Mrs. Wittol, when next you see her.
Samuel Marchbanks.

*

To Chandos Fribble, ESQ.

Dear Fribble:

During the last few days I have received a horrifying number of invitations and supplications from people who want me to join or support something new. They all appear to want to create something which has never been known on earth before. But not me. I am sick of novelties – or what pass for novelties among easily-satisfied people. And for that reason I am organizing a one-man *Society for the Resurrection and Preservation of Words which Have Been Permitted to Lapse into Unmerited Disuse.* Let's deal with something old, for a change.

There are many such words, and from time to time I may issue bulletins about them. But for the time being these will do:

(1) HUZZA: an excellent word which has been dropped in favour of "hurrah." But huzza has a nice, genteel air about it; it expresses enthusiasm, but not too much. It is the ideal word to use when, for instance, somebody suggests that you go for a good long tramp in the country, just as you have settled down for a nap in your chair. It is a good word to shout, in a well-controlled voice, when unpopular officials pass you in a procession. My typewriter ribbon has just broken, and luckily I have another, which I shall have to put in the machine myself, getting my hands dirty and abrading my temper. Huzza!

(2) HOSANNA: another useful word of praise, expressing goodwill without overdoing it. It has hardly been used in ordinary speech since the following limerick was current, around 1905:

> There was a young maiden named Anna
> Who sang as a High Church soprana;
> > When she fell in the aisle
> > The Dean said with a smile,
> "We have heard, now we see, your hosanna!"

(3) HEYDAY: the dictionary calls this "an exclamation of gaiety or surprise." Yes, but not of ecstatic gaiety or complete surprise. This seems to me to be just the word to use when unwrapping a gift of handkerchiefs which looks precisely like handkerchiefs, which has been presented to you by somebody who always gives you handkerchiefs.

Words for the expression of limited emotion are not too common in our language. The three I have listed above should not be allowed to die, and so far as I am concerned, they shan't.

Yours,
Samuel Marchbanks.

*

To Samuel Marchbanks, ESQ.

Dear Mr. Marchbanks:

It is with a heavy heart, Mr. Marchbanks, sir, that I write to tell you that your lawsuit against Richard Dandiprat finally came to court on Tuesday last, and that you have lost it. It was a most unhappy chance that brought a case of such delicacy to the attention of the judge the day after his birthday. His Honour had obviously been keeping the festival in the great tradition, and as soon as he took his place on the bench it was plain that his mind was occupied with old, unhappy, far-off things. Our Mr. Cicero Forcemeat was also somewhat indisposed, having been called to the bar repeatedly the day before; the lustre of his eloquence was, shall we say, dimmed. Dandiprat's lawyers, Craven and Raven, were in like case, and the court presented an hapless picture. Nobody could hear anybody else; everybody was drinking bromoseltzer; the janitor had neglected to turn on the heat. The trial occupied precisely seven and one-half minutes. The judge was annoyed that you were not present, and has fined you $100 for contempt of court. This, with the costs of the suit, will amount to a rather larger figure than you have probably anticipated. But without the Unforeseen, Mr. Marchbanks, life would be intolerable and the law would be an exact science, instead of the tantalizing jade that she is.

A complete statement is enclosed, and prompt payment will be appreciated by

Your most faithful,

Mordecai Mouseman

(for Mouseman, Mouseman and Forcemeat).

*

To Samuel Marchbanks, ESQ.

Well, Sammy Old Pal:

The trial is now over, and no hard feelings, eh? All good pals as before. Drop in any time, and bring your own bottle with you. Like I say to the Little Woman – "No use getting mad at Marchbanks; it takes all kinds to make a world; so let's be big about this thing, Goo-Ball, and forgive him for all the hard things he has thought about us; after all, like the fellow says, he's probably an eight-ulcer man in a four-ulcer job."

By the way, one day when you were out I borrowed your wheelbarrow, and it just came apart in my hands. You can have the pieces back any time, but you'd be better off to get a new one.

All the best for neighbourly relations,

Dick Dandiprat.

*

To Mervyn Noseigh, M.A.

Dear Mr. Noseigh:

Your last question is a humdinger. "When did you first decide to be a humorist; who were your chief humorous influences; how do you define humour?" – you ask, just like that.

I never decided to be a humorist; if I am one, I was born one, but I have never really given the matter much thought. I was once given a medal for humour, but it makes me nervous; I have tried to lose it, but I am too superstitious to throw it away. Men who bother their heads too much about being something particular – a Humorist, or a Philosopher, or a Social Being, or a Scientist, or a Humanist, or whatever – quickly cease to be men and become animated attitudes.

I suppose some of the humorists I have read have influenced me, because I think of them with affection, but never as people to be copied. I have read others, greatly praised as funny-men, who simply disgusted me. If I had to name a favourite, I suppose it would have to be Francois Rabelais, but I do not give him my whole heart; he had a golden touch with giants and pedants, but he thought ignobly of women.

Don't you know what humour is? Universities re-define wit and satire every few years; surely it is time they nailed down humour for us? I don't know what it is, though I suspect that it is an attribute of everything, and the substance of nothing, so if I had to define a sense of humour I would say it lay in the perception of shadows.

Sorry to be so disappointing,
Samuel Marchbanks.

*

To Mrs. Kedijah Scissorbill.

Madam:

So you are astonished that a man of my apparent good sense should believe in astrology, are you? My good woman, if you knew more of my history, you would be astonished that my good sense is still apparent.

You have heard of the Wandering Jew, who roams the earth till Judgement Day? I am his cousin, the Wandering Celt, and my branch of the family is the elder. Therefore I have had a good deal of experience in belief:

In my early days I was invited by learned men to believe in the Triple Goddess, and a very good goddess she was. But when I was Christianized I was commanded to believe in a Trinity that was also a Unity, and a goddess who looked and behaved remarkably like my Triple Goddess, though I was assured she was somebody much more up-to-date and important. Then a man named Calvin demanded that I believe in Strength through Misery, and I did till a man named Wesley told me to believe in Personal Revelation and Ecstasy, and I did. During a brief spell in New England Emerson told me to believe in a Unity that had nothing to do with a Trinity, and was itself of doubtful existence, and I did. But then I was told by people calling themselves scientists to believe in Phrenology, Animal Magnetism, the Germ Theory, Psycho-Analysis, Sociology, Relativity, Atomic Energy, Space Travel, God-is-Dead, Quasars, Spiral Time and so many new faiths that I could not keep up with them, though I tried.

Until I wearied and went back to the Triple Goddess, with Astrology thrown in for fun.

Because as a Celt, you see, I am at once credulous of everything and sceptical of everything, and not a whole-hogger, who rushes from the Mother of God to Mary Baker Eddy, and from her to LSD, expecting some revelation that will settle everything. I don't want everything settled. I enjoy the mess.

So with all the fiery planets opposed to Uranus I am

Yours sincerely,

Samuel Marchbanks.

*

MAUNDERINGS AT NIGHTFALL

VOICE OF REASON / Was talking to a man about politics today, and he expressed several opinions with which I disagreed, gently but firmly. "The trouble with you is that you are disillusioned," he said at last. "No," said I, "that is not true; I can never recall a time when I was illusioned, if you will permit such an expression. Even as a child I had a firm grasp of the fact that human beings are that and nothing more, and that it is unreasonable to expect them to behave like angels. It is unreasonable to expect the uneducated to behave like the educated; it is unreasonable to expect the ethical to behave like the unethical; it is unreasonable to expect the hungry to behave like the replete, the poor like the rich, and the unhappy like the happy. We must not find fault with people because they often fall short of perfect virtue. We may hope for the best, but we should not be unduly downcast when it does not come to pass. A great part of the world's misery is the result of this foolish expectation that people are always going to be on their best behaviour. Man is born sinful; the remarkable thing is not that man fails to be wholly good, but that he is as good as he is." He continued to eye me sadly, but I knew that my Stoicism had got under his skin. But am I wise . . . or just a master of low-pressure platitude?

ODIOUS COMPARISON / Business took me to Ottawa and I reflected, as I do whenever I approach Ottawa by train, that it has a romantic and fairy-tale appearance. I also pondered on the fact that Ottawa, at present, has a population about equal to that of Athens in the days of Pericles, and that a city does not have to be huge in order to be great. It might be argued that great numbers of Athenians were slaves, and it could be replied that great numbers of Ottawans are slaves also, but I cannot see that this alters the comparison in any important way.

VAIN BOAST / There can be no doubt that future historians will look upon this present age as an Age of Decline. True, it will have its glories, and may be referred to in histories of philosophy and humanism as the Age of Marchbanks, but it is scarcely possible for a single man to redeem a whole era. Today, for instance, I found myself in the company of several men of business, and they were boasting, which is no cause for surprise. But of what were they boasting? They were blowing, to my grief and astonishment, about the rate of Income Tax they paid. "Fifty per cent of all I make goes in Income Tax," cried one. "Laughable pauper!" cried another, "I have paid sixty-five per cent for years!" "To the House of Refuge with you!" cried still a third, and revealed that he keeps only fifteen per cent of what he makes. When all men have left to be proud of is the poor moiety which the tax-gatherers leave them of their wealth, a greater decline than that of Imperial Rome is far advanced. Mark the words of Marchbanks the Prophet.

*

COMMUNIQUÉ (*delivered by a Dove with an olive twig in its beak*)

To Big Chief Marchbanks.

How, Marchbanks:

Not out of jail yet, Marchbanks. This awful late Spring. No want freedom. Want jail. So when day come for let me out I kick Turkey awful hard when he inspecting beds. What for you kick me, he say. Seat your pants awful shiny, I say. Dazzle my eyes. Make me think sunrise. I kick for do Sun Dance. Ha, ha. Joke Marchbanks. Turkey get red neck. O, he say, funny fellow huh. Yes, I say. So he say I get no time off for good conduct and have to stay in jail another week. This good, Marchbanks. Maybe Spring in one more week. This awful snow remind me poem my grandmother Old Nokomis teach me.

> March winds
> And April showers
> Always a month late
> In this dam country of ours.

Nokomis fine poet, eh Marchbanks?
    How, again
        Osceola Thunderbelly
        (Chief of the Crokinoles).

*

CULLED FROM THE APOPHTHEGMS
OF WIZARD MARCHBANKS

As Goethe said, it is the Eternal Feminine that beckons us ever onward: he did not mention the Eternal Old Woman who holds us back.

THE AUTHOR

PLAYWRIGHT, novelist, critic, essayist, humourist, former actor, newspaper publisher, Professor of English and Master of Massey College, Robertson Davies is a man of infinite variety. He was born in Thamesville, Ontario, in 1913, the son of the Hon. William Rupert Davies, and the extension of a long line of progeny "... especially lacking in U.E.L. blood."

A long attachment to processes of education began in Renfrew and Kingston schools, and continued through Upper Canada College, Toronto, Queen's University, Kingston, and Balliol College, Oxford, where he received his B.Lit.

Since his return to Canada in 1940 he has been Editor of *Saturday Night*, and of the *Peterborough Examiner*, to which he was appointed Publisher in 1958. He became the first Master of Massey College (at the University of Toronto) when it opened in 1963, a position which he still maintains. He has also become a full professor there, and has acquired a number of other degrees over the years.

Mr. Davies' many plays include *Fortune My Foe*, the best Canadian play at the Dominion Drama Festival of 1949, *At My Heart's Core*, *Hunting Stuart* and *Love and Libel*. He collaborated with Sir Tyrone Guthrie on three books about Ontario's Stratford Shakespearean Festival (of which he is a Governor), and he displays his gifts as an essayist *par excellence* in *A Voice From the Attic*. His other books include three novels, *Tempest Tost*, *Leaven of Malice* and *A Mixture of Frailties*, and two other "Marchbanks" books, *The Diary of Samuel Marchbanks*, and *The Table Talk of Samuel Marchbanks*; his work has appeared in such magazines as *Atlantic Monthly*, *Saturday Evening Post*, and the *New York Times*.

Mr. Davies is married to Brenda Mathews, former Stage Manager of the Old Vic in London, and has three children. He lives in Massey College, and is at present working on his fourth novel, and one volume of a projected *History of Drama in Canada*.

THE NEW CANADIAN LIBRARY